HOUGHTON MIFFLIN

WE THE PEOPLE
Build Our Nation

Assessment Options

Grade 5

Houghton Mifflin Company • Boston
Atlanta • Dallas • Geneva, Illinois • Palo Alto • Princeton

Printed in U.S.A.
ISBN: 0-395-80663-1

8 9 10 11 12 13 14 15 16-HS 05 04 03 02 01 00

Table of Contents

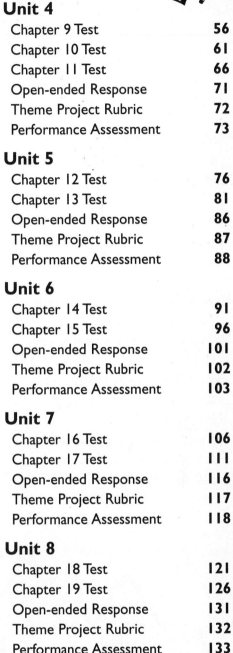

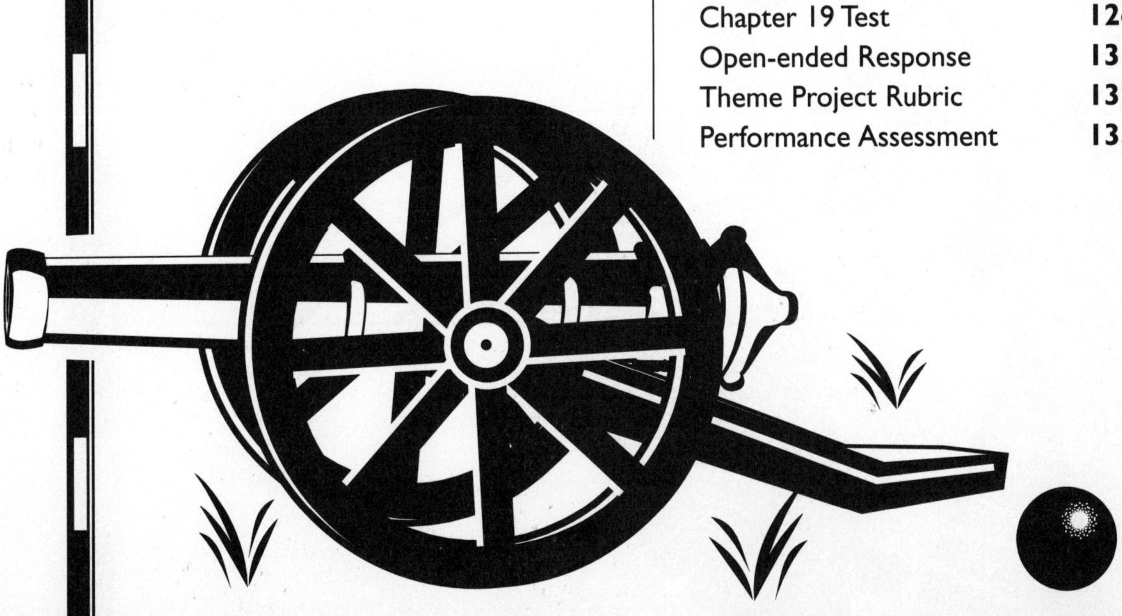

Assessment in *We the People*

Social Studies Assessment Today

Assessment is the process of gathering information to aid in the evaluation of students' academic progress. That evaluation can be useful for both individual and collective decision-making.

Assessment today usually means balanced assessment, which includes—and values—a teacher's informal, day-to-day appraisal as well as more formal documentation of student performance. Thus it allows students to demonstrate their progress in a variety of ways. Balanced assessment is very much an integral part of the curriculum and must reflect and support classroom instruction.

As an ongoing process, balanced assessment tells where each student is at any given time and enables more accurate evaluation at year's end. It measures not only achievements and products but growth and progress. Assessment becomes both a learning and teaching opportunity. It allows you to tailor your instruction to individual needs. It also involves students in the process, encouraging them to set goals and make decisions about their own learning and, ultimately, to become more reflective, critical learners.

Furthermore, balanced assessment is authentic, in that it clearly reflects the stated goals and expected outcomes of instruction—and presumes that students understand what is expected of them. Authentic assessment also involves real-life tasks or challenges. Authenticity assumes that assessment events are contextualized, and requires students to apply their knowledge, skill, and cognitive processing to current, relevant, and enduring issues.

Informal Assessment

Informal assessment utilizes the ongoing observations you make on a daily basis and focuses on the processes that students use as well as the products they create.

Any of the following may become elements in your informal assessment process: anecdotal notes, checklists and forms, oral presentations, performance assessment, conferences, interviews, conversations, journal entries, learning logs. Keep in mind that not all assessment activities need to be done for all students at all times.

Informal assessment also involves students in the evaluation of their own learning process. While teachers are informally assessing students, students are assessing themselves as learners and can contribute insights that may help shape your instructional plans.

Formal Assessment

Formal assessment provides a "snapshot" of each student at a given time and often includes pencil-and-paper assessment instruments such as chapter tests. In a balanced assessment program, formal test results are one important component of the total assessment picture. Indeed, you may want to "test" the test results of your students against what you see in your observations and in their portfolios, presentations, and group work.

While pencil-and-paper tests continue to be a traditional format for formal assessment, formal assessment instruments are more and more including assessment activities that reflect instructional activities—for example, real-world writing activities such as letters, newspaper editorials, and speeches.

Formal observation of activities is not just something the teacher does; it can also be something that students prepare for and that both the teacher and students discuss. Students should usually be informed that an activity is going to be observed formally. Scoring criteria, whether in the format of a checklist or a scoring rubric, can be given to students in advance. The first time students try an activity that will be formally assessed—whether group oral presentation or a simulation—they may welcome the opportunity to practice without observation.

Self-Assessment

Involving students in the assessment and evaluation process is an essential part of balanced assessment. When students become partners in the learning process, they gain a better sense of themselves as learners and thinkers. As students reflect on what they have learned and how they learn it, they develop the tools to become more effective learners. As they examine their work, they can think about what they do well and in which areas they still need help. If you provide students with criteria or target behaviors, they will have the framework they may need for successful self-examination.

Portfolio Assessment

Portfolio assessment is a long-term approach to ongoing assessment that offers opportunities to monitor students' changing progress throughout the year. The collection of student products in a portfolio provide an overview of students' intellectual capabilities and academic experiences. Portfolios can help you focus on the growth of the individual over time rather than how the student's performance compares to that of his or her peers.

Portfolios can be highly personalized, as would be the case when an artist creates his or her own portfolio and makes all the decisions about content and presentation. On the other hand, they can be quite standardized, if a standard format is required by an individual teacher, school, district, or state. The decision as to the intended purpose of the portfolios will determine the kind of assessment tool the portfolios will become. You may want to work with other teachers to develop evaluation criteria of portfolios.

As you revisit portfolio entries with your students, you may want to encourage them to continue a work-in-progress, revise or improve a draft, expand or extend a brief assignment, or look at a product as a basis of comparison for a similar piece of work. Portfolios also give you an opportunity to share an overview of a student's work with families, with other teachers, or with school administrators. In some school systems, teachers may pass students' portfolios on to the next-year teacher.

Open-ended Questions

Balanced assessment includes asking students open-ended questions—prompts for which there is no single correct or predetermined response—as well as fixed-response questions. Open-ended questions allow students to incorporate their personal beliefs and experiences as they develop a thoughtful and reasonable response. Students may be asked to use and analyze information to draw conclusions and make a judgment, or to use their knowledge creatively and imaginatively in the context of real-world applications.

Open-ended questions are obviously antithetical to fixed-response questions. Nonetheless, they can be graded objectively if instructional objectives are stated clearly and if task instructions include clearly stated scoring criteria. After reading the instructions, students should be able to tell what is expected and how they will be scored.

Performance Assessment

Performance assessment events are hands-on, authentic activities that help evaluate students' understanding of a concept and/or mastery of skills. The design of performance assessment events reflects many of the same principles as open-ended questions, such as targeting directly the stated objectives of the unit. These activities give students an opportunity to demonstrate creatively their understanding of concepts and skills and indeed to use their full repertoire of related knowledge and skills. Well-designed performance events accommodate varied learning styles and are relevant and interesting to students. Criteria for completing the activity should be identified, shared with students, and used for evaluating the product. When appropriate, you may want to have students work together on performance assessment activities.

Integrating Assessment and Instruction

We the People

As educators set higher academic expectations for all students, it is extremely important that we re-examine the means of evaluating student progress toward and mastery of those expectations. The assessment program of *We the People* is both innovative and based on solid research—and it reflects what teachers have shared with us about what they believe is useful and comfortable.

We the People integrates multiple formats of assessment in the Teacher's Books, Student Book, and blackline master components. You have always been the best evaluator of your students' progress and attainments, so this variety of formats offers you the flexibility of choosing how best to assess each student's work in a meaningful way, depending on your classroom needs. And all assessment components have been tested against standards of high interest, multicultural inclusion, and sensitivity.

Student Book

In an assessment program clearly derived from instructional objectives, students must know he objectives of the chapter and know that any assessment of their progress will relate directly to those objectives—no more and no less. In *We the People,* each lesson in the Student Book begins with a clearly stated Main Idea, and the Key Vocabulary and Key Events of the lesson are highlighted as well. Then a Focus Question, correlated with each Lesson Objective in the Teacher's Book, frames each section of a lesson for the student reader.

The Lesson Review invites students to write down their answers to each Focus Question in the lesson just studied. This process allows students to monitor their own learning and revisit each section of the lesson as necessary before they proceed to the next lesson or chapter. The Lesson Review also provides an opportunity to check for students' understanding of the Key Vocabulary taught in the lesson, with additional questions that encourage students to think critically about lesson content and to make connections to citizenship, geography, or the unit theme.

Then the Chapter Review ties together the lessons of the chapter. Students summarize the chapter's main idea, review vocabulary and key facts, and check their mastery of geography and map skills, visual learning, and research skills. The critical thinking questions in the Chapter Review provide opportunities for students to interpret and think analytically about their growing knowledge and skills, to make generalizations and draw conclusions based on them, and to apply them to new ideas or problems.

The activity at the end of each Lesson Review, as well as the activities in the Chapter Review, provide a variety of open-ended prompts and opportunities for performance assessment. These activities connect social studies strands such as geography and citizenship with cross-curricular disciplines such as art, science, and writing. Each Chapter Review also provides a checkpoint for students to monitor their progress through the on-going Theme Project for the unit.

Teacher's Book

Each lesson in the Teacher's Book begins with a list of Lesson Objectives (desired learning outcomes) chosen to emphasize the big picture. Lesson Objectives correspond to Focus Questions in the Student Books, which are worded in student-friendly language to let student readers focus on what is important for them to learn and know. On the Chapter Tests (in Assessment Options), questions have evolved from the lesson objectives—assessing the major content and skills that is most important for students to learn. Correlations to Lesson Objectives are coded in the Answer Key of Assessment Options.

The Teacher's Book of *We the People* suggests ways to check student progress and understanding—for example, referring students to the Focus Question for a section of a lesson or using the Lesson Review to assess understanding of the lesson. Informal Assessment tips as well as Portfolio Opportunities and Self-Assessment suggestions appear in the lower corners of Teacher's Book pages for lessons and special features.

In *We the People,* the Teacher's Book is rich with opportunities for activity-based instruction and cooperative learning, but the choice is up to you as to which activities to assign or how many activities belong in your year-long curriculum. The teaching plan is flexible enough to allow you to customize a program of social studies activities to meet the needs of a particular classroom or year, including addressing a variety of learning styles.

Any of the Cross-Curricular Activities, which are provided in the Teacher's Book at the beginning of each chapter, as well as the many activities provided below the facsimiles of student lesson pages can be used for performance assessment, as triggers for portfolio products, or as opportunities for self-assessment or peer assessment. Many recurrent types of activities can be assessed by using the appropriate Multiple-use Masters in *Assessment Options*—see below.

Assessment Options Masters

The *Assessment Options* booklet of assessment masters gives you a variety of forms of assessment designed to allow you to choose how best to assess your students' growth and progress in social studies (see below).

Other Blackline Masters

The array of blackline master components in *We the People* provides additional ways to integrate assessment throughout your social studies program. For example, communicating with students' families is an important part of involving families with their students' school experience and letting them know how well their students are doing. Home and Community Involvement offers many suggestions for establishing and maintaining contact with families throughout the school year, providing a Parent-Teacher Conference Checklist and a Post-Conference Action plan as well as Letters to Families, Family Newsletters, and much more material. In Skills Workshop and Geography Activities, the reinforcement and extension activity sheets and Outline Maps can lend themselves to your assessment purposes and make excellent portfolio opportunities. And the cooperative experiences in Citizenship Simulations are worthwhile opportunities for performance assessment that make students think, incorporate group effort, and call for students to apply their social studies knowledge to decision-making, resolving conflict, and participation.

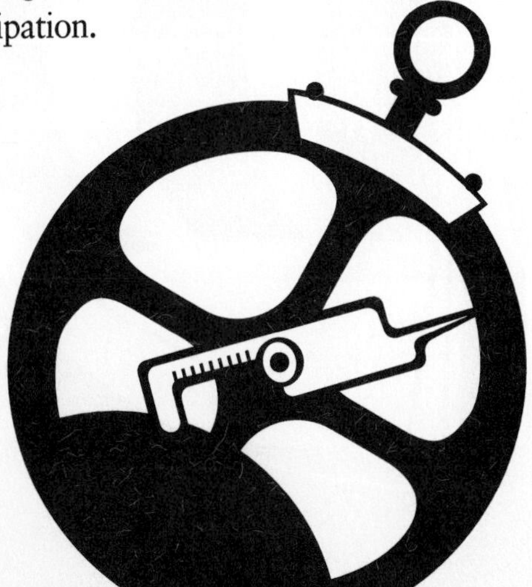

Using *Assessment Options*: Chapter and Unit Assessment

Assessment Options provides masters for both chapter- and unit-level assessment. You may also want to use the Multiple-Use Masters to support performance assessment and portfolio assessment (see below).

Chapter Tests

The objectives from each lesson in a chapter have guided test writing, making what will be tested—important concepts and ideas and not trivial detail—predictable to both teacher and students. Chapter Tests assess comprehension, analysis, and application by addressing not just recall of bare facts but understanding of facts, concepts, and skills. Critical thinking is nurtured throughout the *We the People* program and encouraged in assessment as well. Visual prompts—such as maps, time lines, and charts—challenge students to use their knowledge of chapter content to analyze, synthesize, or interpret the information so presented.

Each Chapter Test provides a balance of fixed response questions and free response questions. The answer key at the back of this booklet provides answers to fixed response questions and sample answers to free response questions.

On the last page of each Chapter Test, students are always assessed on their mastery of the skill taught in the chapter's Skills Workshop feature. Attention is paid to the thinking processes of students as they are asked to apply a map skill, visual learning skill, or social studies research skill in the context of chapter-related content. And with the skills questions placed at the end of the test, you can choose to have students stop just short of the skills questions, depending on your instructional needs.

Open-ended Response (Unit Assessment)

Open-ended Responses require an extended written product, sometimes supplemented by visual representations. Students are asked to pull together information they have learned throughout the entire unit to make connections to the unit's theme. Questions are constructed to be clear and compelling, and many give students choices of how to answer, honoring varied learning styles and interests.

Theme Project Rubrics (Unit Assessment)

As each unit opens, students are introduced to the Theme Project and called upon to use their full repertoire of related knowledge and skills in activities extending over the time period of the entire unit. Supplementing the Simplified Scoring Rubrics presented in the Teacher's Book, each Theme Project Rubric master in Assessment Options is a complete four-level scoring rubric for holistic assessment of these free-ranging, loosely structured student projects.

Performance Assessment (Unit Assessment)

Less ambitious than a Theme Project, a Performance Assessment Event in *Assessment Options* provides a culminating, thematic assessment opportunity for each unit. Scoring criteria are included in the task instructions for these relevant and high-interest activities. Depending on your preference, your students can complete the performance event solely in the classroom or with take-home stages or library research, and as individuals, with partners, or in small groups. Extension options are offered on the student-instruction sheet as well as on the Performance Assessment Tips page, which gives the teacher suggestions and support in implementing the assessment event. The third master for each performance event is a four-level Performance Assessment Rubric, which was developed from the criteria given to students when they are assigned the task.

Using *Assessment Options:* Multiple-Use Assessment Masters

Suppose your students are engaged in small group discussions about an issue or decision-making about a problem; role-playing a mock trial or a business-union negotiation; creating a narrative account of a typical day of a 19th century pioneer; or writing a poem about a landform. How can you assess work such as this? The Multiple-Use Masters—checklists and observation records—support your evaluation of an array of recurrent types of performance events and portfolio products that may be part of your students' learning social studies.

Evaluation by the Teacher

Each multiple-use master includes a checklist with a rating scale as well as options for you to record specific constructive criticism or suggestions for improvement. Evaluation sheets are ideal for student-teacher conferences to follow an activity such as oral presentations. For products that will be included in your students' portfolios, you may want to complete and attach the appropriate evaluation sheets and then share them with parents when you show them their children's work.

Peer Assessment

For activities in which individual students or groups present their work to the entire class as audience, peer assessment with Multiple-Use Masters can be an appropriate means of giving students feedback. Sharing their ideas about how to improve the work of other students can help students improve their own work. You may want to rotate the responsibility of peer assessment among students in your class.

Self-Assessment

Through the activities and products you assign, students will have many opportunities to show you their ideas and understanding of content as well as their mastery of social studies skills. By letting them use Multiple-Use Masters to share their thoughts about the outcomes of their work and how they would improve it, you can encourage them to participate as willing partners in their own assessment.

Scoring Rubrics

For many difficult-to-score student products, scoring rubrics can look holistically at the whole work, the completed work, rather than cumulatively grading elements of the work. Teachers can review the entirety of a student product and decide in general which description in the rubric most closely fits the work being evaluated.

Holistic assessment is always designed to score student work against an expected standard of performance as well as to reveal if students are growing and extending. This approach to assessment can be used to encourage students to revisit or revise work, especially for major assignments. Rubrics should also be flexible enough to allow for an imaginative or creative student who might take alternative or novel approaches.

Based on pre-stated scoring criteria—expected standards of student performance—scoring rubrics are designed to make scoring of activities, projects, and varied products easier and less subjective. And scoring rubrics are great tools to use with students and parents who question how a task was scored.

In *Assessment Options,* a Performance Assessment Rubric accompanies the Performance Assessment Event at the end of each unit, and a Theme Project Rubric is also provided (see above).

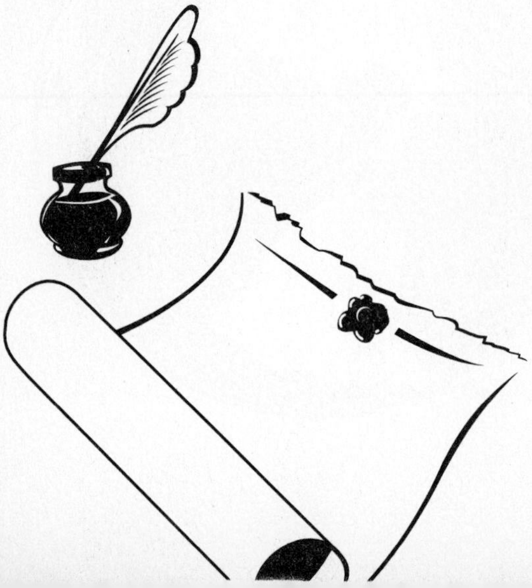

Tips for Creating or Adapting Your Own Rubrics

Developing your own rubrics for the work done in your classroom can be rewarding and enriching for you and your students. Approaching this task is as easy as following this plan.

A good way to start is to work with others. Ask your faculty colleagues to do the same activities with their students. Discuss the criteria against which you will assess students' work. Before your students begin an activity or project, let them know what you consider complete work, using the criteria you discussed with your colleagues. Have your students do the activity. When they are done, gather up the results of their work.

With your colleagues, discuss and sort the students' products into groups. Together you will get a broader perspective to help you create the rubric. If you are comfortable involving your students, have them help sort products into groups. You may wish to cover up the names of students on the papers so that you and the students will look at the work more objectively. Four groups work well, with a rating of Level 4 for the best work and a rating of Level 1 for work that shows little or no understanding, but your rubrics can have five or six levels.

Discuss with students the characteristics of the responses and allow them to be a part of the process of developing criteria for a Level 4 category. Then articulate rubrics for the other levels, and list the qualifications. Examples of student work can and should be shared to help students understand the standards applied to their work. Some things to consider as you create the four groups can be found on the Generic Rubric, below.

Generic Rubric

The following sample rubric describes various levels of student work from the most to the least successful. You may want to use it as a model for creating your own rubrics.

Level 4 Well done/ Outstanding

- The project demonstrates solid understanding of social studies concepts and content.
- Student followed all directions correctly. The project exhibits breadth or depth, either addressing all or many aspects of the assignment or developing certain aspects of the assignment with special creativity.
- Explanations are accurate and thorough. Students have made connections, identified relationships, analyzed causes, and creatively applied their reasoning in appropriate material.
- The work clearly shows the student's ideas. Presentation is polished, with evidence of revision.
- The work reflects excellent application of relevant social studies skills.

Level 3 Acceptable/ Satisfactory

- The project demonstrates a satisfactory understanding of social studies concepts and content. Content errors are relatively minor.
- Students have mostly followed all directions. Although some minor elements may be missing, the project addresses key aspects of assignment and essentially achieves the task as expected.
- Explanations are essentially correct but could be clearer. Students show evidence that they have used thinking skills, made connections, and applied their understandings in appropriate material.
- The work is generally orderly. Presentation shows evidence of revision, but might benefit from more polishing.
- The student has applied relevant social studies skills as expected for this grade level.

Level 2 Less than satisfactory/ Revision needed

- The project suggests some misunderstanding of social studies concepts and content. While there is correct material, there are some major content errors.
- Student efforts may have been somewhat misdirected. The project does not address all aspects of the assignment, or some work is included that does not relate directly to the assignment.
- Students may have attempted to make connections but explanations are unclear or logic faulty.
- The work is not presented well and lacks organization. Insufficient attention has been paid to communicating with an audience. Significant revisions are required to create an acceptable product.
- The student has not successfully applied all relevant social studies skills, or has done so with mistakes.

Level 1 Unacceptable/ Restart

- The project misses the social studies content and suggests that the student has fragmented or superficial understanding. Either the student is having great difficulty with content or has not completed enough work to show understanding.
- The work presented fails in significant ways to meet the assignment. The student may not understand directions or expectations or has not put in much effort. If the student could restart the task, he or she would need special teacher support or one-on-one help.
- Connections between concepts are not made or are illogical. There is little evidence that sound thinking skills have been applied.
- The work is poorly presented. An audience would have difficulty understanding the product.
- There is little or no evidence that the student has applied the necessary social studies skills to the assignment.

Name ______________________________ Date ________________

Chapter 1 Test

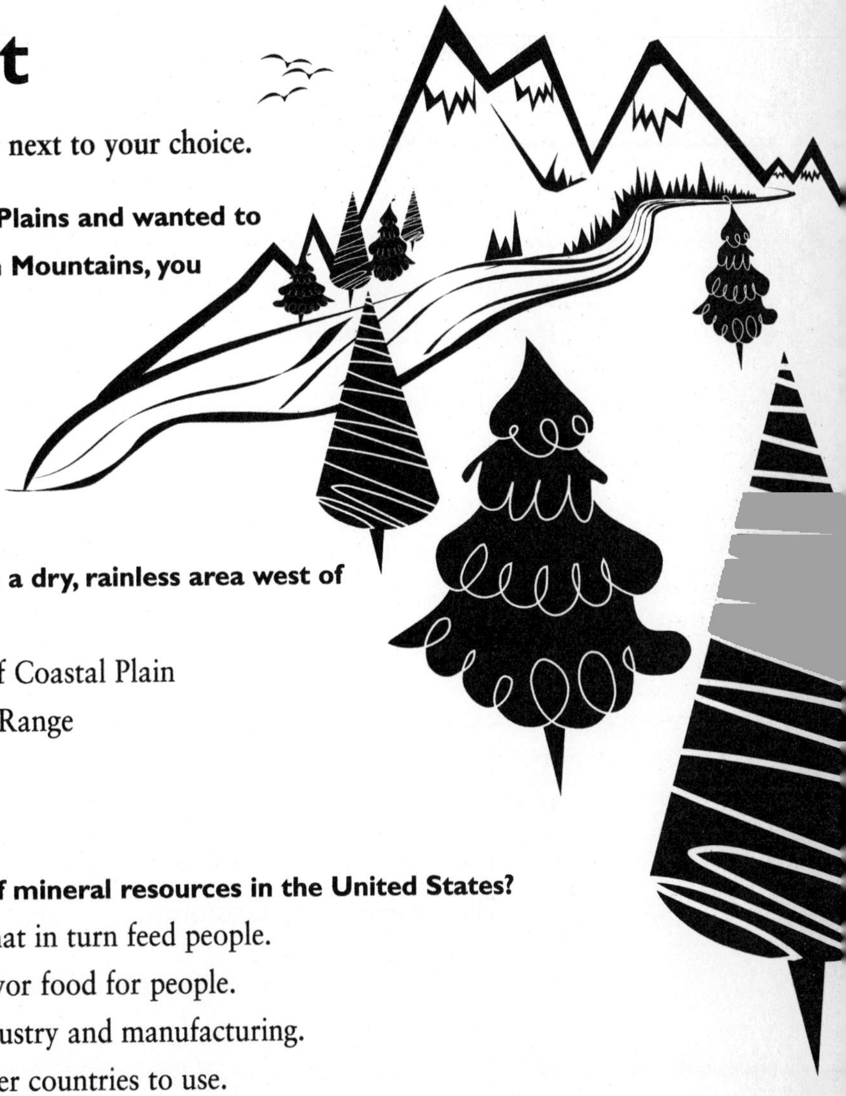

Choose the best answer. Circle the letter next to your choice.

1. If you were in the Great Plains and wanted to travel to the Appalachian Mountains, you would go MOSTLY —

A. north
B. south
C. east
D. west

2. Which of the following is a dry, rainless area west of the Rocky Mountains?

A. the Atlantic and Gulf Coastal Plain
B. the Great Basin and Range
C. the Cascades Range
D. the Interior Plains

3. What is the major use of mineral resources in the United States?

A. They feed animals that in turn feed people.
B. They are used to flavor food for people.
C. They are used in industry and manufacturing.
D. They are sold to other countries to use.

4. What is the BIGGEST problem our country faces with its water resources?

A. The supply is quickly running out in all regions.
B. We pollute water faster than we can clean it.
C. Most people prefer to drink other kinds of beverages.
D. The amount that is available varies from year to year.

5. Why do geographers divide land into regions?

A. to make the geography of a large area easier to understand
B. to study the animals and plants that belong in one place
C. to be sure that everything gets placed on maps
D. to try to control the weather in different parts of the country

Name ______________________________ Date ____________________

6. Silicon Valley is the name given to an area in California where the computer industry is very important. Given this information, what kind of region is the Silicon Valley?

A. a region defined by its location

B. a region defined by a physical feature

C. an economic region

D. a climate region

7. Why does the United States have so many different human and cultural regions?

A. because it is made up of fifty different states

B. because its people come from many different backgrounds

C. because its people have the same form of government

D. because different geographers define regions in different ways

8. What is true about the people in ANY cultural region?

A. They have a shared way of life.

B. They are all immigrants.

C. They make their living in the same way.

D. They like the same landforms.

9. Which of the following is MOST affected by the climate we live in?

A. the holidays we celebrate

B. the way we build our homes

C. the subjects we study in school

D. the amount of television we watch

10. People MOST OFTEN build cities —

A. on top of a mountain where the view is good

B. on islands where the supply of salt water is plentiful

C. near natural resources, such as water, timber, or minerals

D. in the desert where the climate is dry

Name ______________________ Date ______________

11. How has technology changed the relationship between humans and the environment?

A. People can't change the environment; they have to learn to live with it.
B. People can now change the environment in both good and bad ways.
C. Thanks to technology, people don't need the environment.
D. Before technology, people were better at controlling the environment.

12. Some people oppose building more dams. The MAIN reason they oppose dams is that dams —

A. attract too many tourists
B. create too much power
C. break easily and cause flooding
D. harm the environment

For questions 13–19, choose a word from the list below that matches the description. Write the word in the space provided.

plateau	**region**	**diverse**	**immigrant**
culture	**irrigation**	**basin**	**mineral**
landform	**geographer**	**reservoir**	

13. a low-lying area surrounded by higher land ______________

14. a person who comes to a new place or country to live ______________

15. the language, beliefs, customs, and tools of a group of people ______________

16. a substance mined from the earth ______________

17. a lake where water is stored for use ______________

18. physical feature of the earth's surface ______________

19. a method used to water land ______________

Name ______________________ Date ______________

Use the map to answer questions 20 and 21.

20. Put an X on an area of the United States where irrigation is widely used to grow crops.

21. Put an X on a state in the Midwest.

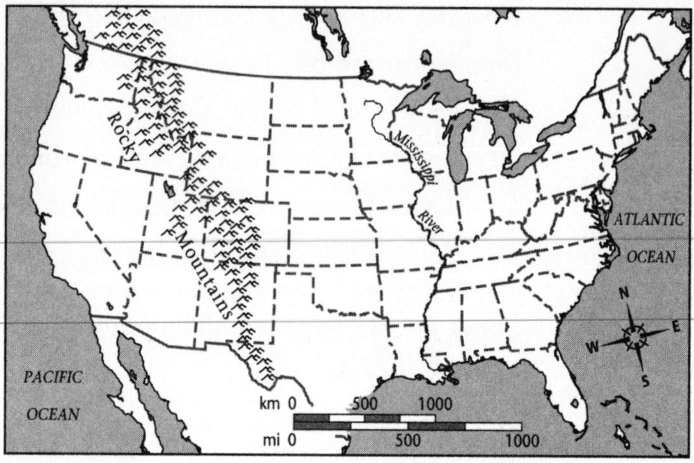

Answer questions 22–27 in the spaces provided. Continue your answer on the back of the sheet if you need to.

22. Name and describe THREE kinds of landforms. ______________________

____

23. How has its supply of natural resources shaped the U.S. economy?

____

24. If someone asked you what region you live in, could you give more than one answer? Explain why.

____

25. Think of the cultural region where you live and the way of life there. Choose a holiday that is part of your way of life. Explain how it is part of your culture.

____

26. Explain how the buildings in your region are influenced by the climate.

____

27. Using the Hoover Dam as an example, explain how people can now change the environment in ways that have both good and bad effects.

____

Name ______________________ Date ______________

The maps show population density in 1890 (*left*) and 1990 (*right*). Use the map skills you have learned to answer questions 28–30.

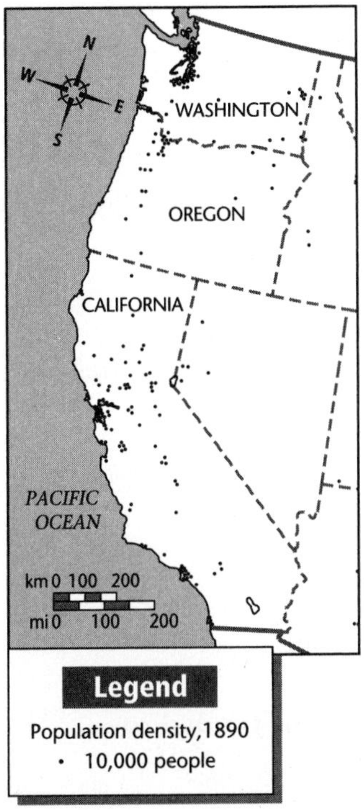

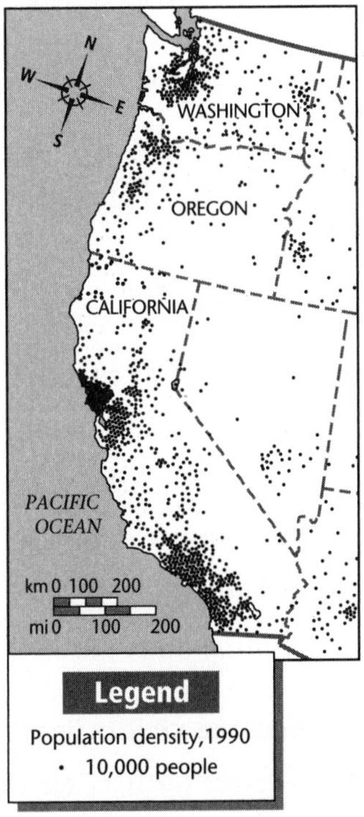

28. In 1890 which state had the area with the densest population?

____

29. Describe how the population density of the West Coast changed between 1890 and 1990.

____

____

30. California is more densely populated than Oregon and Washington. Give ONE likely explanation for this difference.

____

____

Name ______________________ Date ______________

Chapter 2 Test

Choose the best answer. Circle the letter next to your choice.

1. The first Americans probably came here from —

A. Africa

B. Europe

C. Greenland

D. Asia

2. After the weather changed at the end of the Ice Age, how did the hunting patterns of the first Americans change?

A. They learned to stampede huge animals like mammoths over cliffs.

B. They used lighter weapons for smaller game.

C. They no longer hunted.

D. They started hunting large sea animals such as whales.

3. As early cultures became civilizations, their populations tended to —

A. shrink because fewer farmers were needed

B. remain roughly the same size

C. grow because there was extra food

D. fall quickly due to disease

4. Which of the following civilizations was based on warfare and the conquest of farming peoples?

A. The Mound Builders

B. The Anasazi

C. The Aztecs

D. The Mayans

5. The many groups of Native Americans in the Eastern Woodlands shared —

A. an environment of forests, wildlife, and water

B. a single style of building

C. the use of the ocean as their main food source

D. a common language and a common culture

Name ______________________________ Date ________________

6. How were Creek towns governed?

A. by ruling families

B. by the distant Creek Confederacy

C. by religious leaders who had visions during the Green Corn Dance

D. by townspeople and the leader they chose

7. Why did Native Americans on the Pacific coast NOT farm?

A. Their land was too dry to support farming.

B. Enslaved people farmed for them.

C. They found plenty of food by hunting and gathering.

D. They lacked the tools and knowledge to farm.

8. In Hopi life, what were kachinas?

A. playthings used by children

B. spirits that carried messages and prayers to the gods

C. rulers who made decisions about important daily matters

D. a Native American group from the Great Basin area

9. Which of the following groups could best be described as hunters and gatherers?

A. The Pueblo Indians

B. The Plains Indians

C. The Creek

D. The Mississippian

10. For Native Americans who farmed, which crop was typically the most important?

A. Potatoes

B. Wheat

C. Rice

D. Corn

Name ____________________ Date ____________

Choose a word from the list below that matches the description. Write the word in the space provided.

archaeologist	**pueblo**	**glacier**
surplus	**empire**	**confederacy**
drought	**civilization**	

11. **a thick sheet of slowly moving ice** ____________________

12. **a large group made up of many smaller groups** ____________________

13. **an extra amount, to store or trade** ____________________

14. **a long period of time with almost no rain** ____________________

15. **a Spanish word meaning "town"** ____________________

For questions 16 and 17, choose the appropriate letter on the map.

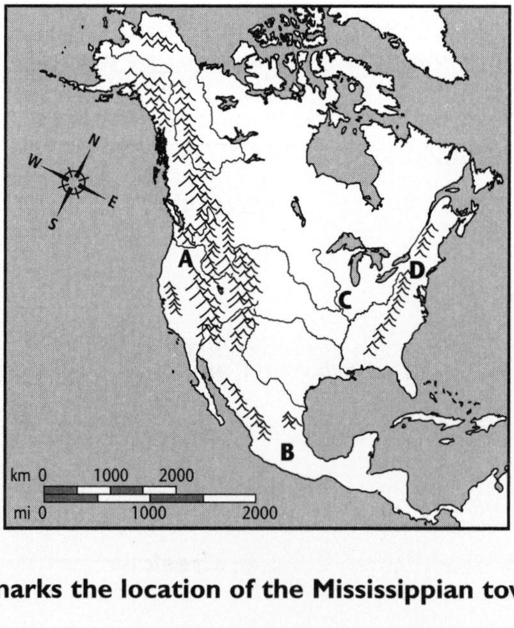

16. **Which letter marks the location of the Mississippian town of Cahokia?**

____

17. **Which letter marks the location of the Aztec capital of Tenochtitlán?**

____

Name ______________________________ Date ________________

Answer questions 18–25 in the spaces provided. Continue your answer on the back of the sheet if you need to.

18. **The first people to migrate to the Americas probably came across a land bridge between Russia and Alaska. What reason best explains their migration?**

____

19. **About 10,000 years ago, the Ice Age ended, and people had to adapt to changes in their way of life. Describe two changes in the types of tools people used.**

____

____

20. **How did life become more diverse as the towns and cities of the first American civilizations arose?**

____

____

21. **How did the climate of the Southwest shape Anasazi farming practices?**

____

22. **Describe the houses built by Native Americans of the eastern woodlands.**

____

____

23. **What role did central plazas play in Creek life?**

____

____

Name ______________________________ Date ________________

24. **What evidence supports the idea that Northwest Indians were wealthy?**

____

25. **Name a belief shared by both the Navaho and Apache.**

____

Use your skills and what you have learned about reading timelines to answer questions 26–29. The questions are based on this timeline, which shows the dates for the Anasazi culture in the southwestern part of North America.

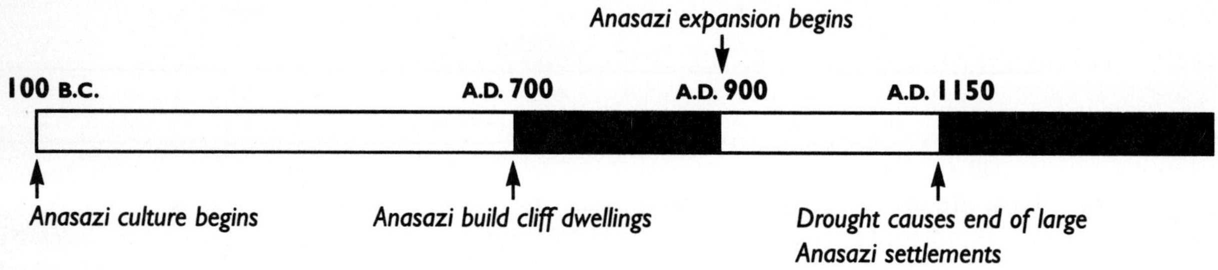

26. **Did Anasazi culture begin about A.D. 100 or 100 B.C. ?**

____

27. **When did Anasazi expansion begin?** ______________________

____

28. **In which century did drought cause the end of the large Anasazi settlements?**

____

29. **About how many years passed from the beginning of Anasazi culture to the end of large Anasazi settlements?**

____

Name ______________________ Date ______________

Open-ended Response

In this unit, you have learned about America's varied landscape and about how Native Americans have depended on the land. Use what you have learned to answer the following question.

How has the way a particular group of people live been shaped by the land and its resources? You may use a Native American group in the past or present; you may also use another group of people in North America today. You can express your answer by writing a paragraph or making a list. You can also draw a picture with labels that explain how the land is used.

Use the lines below for your notes. Prepare your response on separate sheets.

Theme Project Rubric

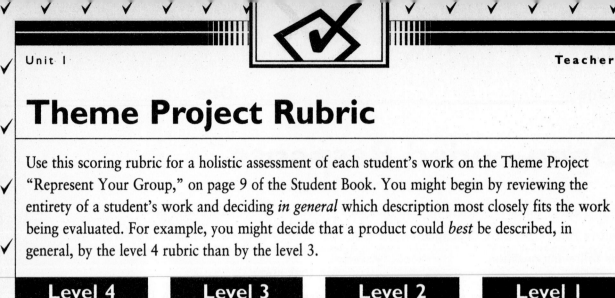

Use this scoring rubric for a holistic assessment of each student's work on the Theme Project "Represent Your Group," on page 9 of the Student Book. You might begin by reviewing the entirety of a student's work and deciding *in general* which description most closely fits the work being evaluated. For example, you might decide that a product could *best* be described, in general, by the level 4 rubric than by the level 3.

Level 4	Level 3	Level 2	Level 1
• The project demonstrates thorough and in-depth knowledge of a specific Native American group in the 1500s, including the group's region, culture, and use of resources. • The project includes many of the following: a map, illustrations, written explanations, and physical artifacts (gifts). • The materials do all of the following well: identify relationships, analyze causes, synthesize a variety of facts, include only material appropriate to the project. • Maps are clear and easily readable, writing is clear and well-organized, gifts have authentic appearance. • The work reflects excellent application of map making and research skills.	• The project demonstrates knowledge of a specific Native American group in the 1500s, including the group's use of resources. • The project includes several types of work, such as a map, illustrations, written explanations, and physical artifacts (gifts). • The project does some of the following: identify relationships, analyze causes, include appropriate material. • The materials are mostly easy to read and are fairly well-organized, with appropriate titles and labels. Gifts have some realistic features. • The materials reflect the relevant social studies skills of constructing maps and using source materials.	• The project shows a misunderstanding of the Native American group, the time period, or the use of resources. • The project includes only one or two types of work or some work that does not relate directly to the Native American group selected. • The project needs revising to identify relationships, analyze causes, and exclude inappropriate materials. • The materials are difficult to read and are poorly organized. Titles and labels are missing or unclear. • The materials demonstrate distinct weaknesses in map making and research skills.	• The project shows a fundamental misunderstanding of both Native American groups and of resource use. • The work presented fails in significant ways to meet the assignment. • The connection between cultural group and resource use is either not made or is illogical. There is little evidence of understanding relationships or causal analysis. • The materials are difficult to read; no organization is evident. Map is missing or features are not recognizable. • The materials provide little or no evidence of map making or research skills.

Name ______________________ Date ______________

Performance Assessment Event

Your teacher will give you directions for using this page.

In this unit, you have learned about America's varied landscape and plentiful resources. You have learned about how Native Americans lived on this land. For this event, you will prepare a visual presentation that compares the past, present, and future uses of our land. Your presentation can be made up of drawings, photographs, maps, charts, or a combination of two or more of those. You can chose any part of America that you like: your home area, a national park, a beautiful lake, or some other place.

Show this place and its resources at three different times: about 1500, in the present, and in the future. For the future, use your knowledge and your imagination. Label each part of your presentation.

Here is what your teacher will look for in evaluating your presentation:

1. Do you show what the land is like and what Native Americans have lived there?
2. Do you show the land in the past, present, and future?
3. Do you clearly show how the land and its resources have been used by people?
4. Is your presentation clear and well labeled, so that people will understand what you are trying to show?

Possible Extensions

A. Find classmates who have chosen the same area or a similar one. Plan a panel discussion to present the past, present, and future of your area.

Your panel discussion will be judged by the following criteria:

1. accuracy and completeness of information
2. ease in following the discussion
3. style and organization of the discussion
4. participation of all panel members

B. What major changes have taken place in the area you have chosen? Create a cause-and-effect diagram to show why some of those changes have occurred.

Performance Assessment Tips

Performance Event

If your students have completed the Theme Project for Unit 1, encourage them to review the maps they made and the material they wrote about resource use. They should also look at their research on Native American artifacts.

Suggest that students consider a number of places before choosing one to depict. Remind them to consider what they know about how the place once looked and how it looks today. The whole class can discuss wise use of resources. Students can brainstorm a list of natural resources and put the list on the board. Also, discuss problems involving these resources.

With help from the class, create a resource table that students can use in planning visuals. Possible resources include atlases, reference books on Native Americans, material on present-day use of resources, and books of artwork and photographs.

Review how to create interesting visuals. Have students discuss the importance of appropriate labels. Suggest that students prepare rough sketches of their visuals. They should share these sketches with a classmate for feedback.

For work needing revision, provide clear directions. Help students decide if the problem is a lack of information, poor selection of area, difficulty in creating visuals, or some other problem. Solicit student suggestions on ways to remedy the problem. For students who must restart, have them come up with a plan for accomplishing the task. Once you have approved the plan, they can start to carry it out. Be sure to monitor their progress regularly.

Extensions

A. Review what a panel discussion involves. Have students work with classmates who have chosen the same area or a similar one. Explain that students have to divide topics among the panelists. Suggest that students rehearse their panel discussion before presenting it to the class. Evaluate students according to the criteria on the student page.

B. Review how to construct a cause-and-effect diagram. Suggest that students focus on two or three changes. Remind them that a change can have multiple causes. When students have finished their diagrams, have them share them with the class.

Performance Assessment Rubric

Use this scoring rubric for a holistic assessment of each student's work on the Performance Assessment Event on page 13 of Assessment Options. You might begin by reviewing the entirety of a student's work and deciding *in general* which description most closely fits the work being evaluated. For example, you might decide that a product could *best* be described, in general, by the level 4 rubric rather than the level 3.

Level 4	Level 3	Level 2	Level 1
• The presentation shows thorough knowledge of landforms, resources, and Native American groups. • The three visuals clearly present the past, present, and future use of the selected location. • The visuals relate use to the land; they show respect for the environment. • Materials are clearly presented and well-labeled. • The presentation shows excellent application of such social studies skills as using source materials, creating maps or graphics, and making predictions.	• The presentation demonstrates satisfactory knowledge of landforms, resources, and Native American groups. • Most required elements are present. • The visuals show land and resource use but the connection is not always obvious. • Material is clear, although some labels are lacking. • The student has adequately applied social studies skills such as using source materials, creating maps or graphics, and making predictions.	• The presentation demonstrates weak knowledge of landforms, resource use, and Native American groups. There are errors or omissions in content. • A number of required elements are missing. • The connection between land use and resources is not made clear. • The presentation is difficult to follow. • There is some evidence of the application of relevant social studies skills.	• The presentation indicates a lack of understanding of landforms, resource use, and Native American groups. • Only one visual, or an incomplete set of visuals, was presented. • The project shows little or no evidence of sound thinking skills. The material presented is illogical. • Visual material is presented in such a way that an audience would have difficulty understanding it. • Use of relevant social studies skills is not evident.

Name ______________________________ Date ________________

Chapter 3 Test

Choose the best answer. Circle the letter next to your choice.

Use the map to answer questions 1 and 2.

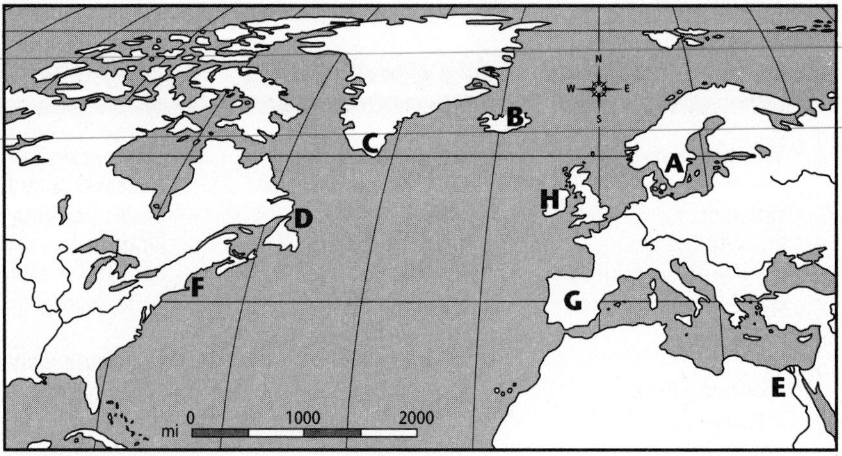

1. Which letter on the map shows where Leif Ericson sailed FROM when he sailed to North America?

A. A B. H C. C D. E

2. Which letter on the map shows where Leif Ericson arrived in North America?

A. D B. F C. G D. B

3. What resources did Vikings find in Greenland that encouraged settlement there?

A. fodder
B. wood
C. ivory from walrus
D. marble

Name ____________________ Date ____________

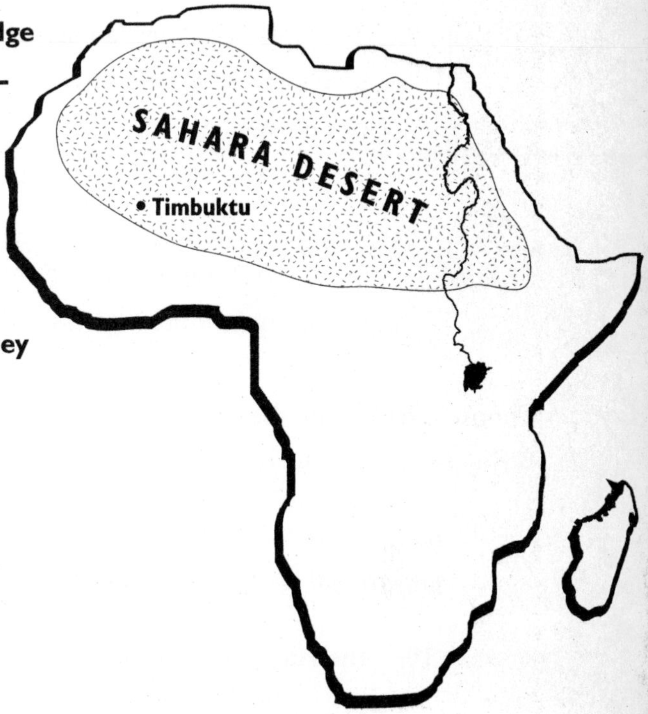

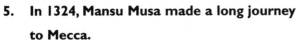

4. The city of Timbuktu, located on the edge of the Sahara, was MAINLY known as —

A. a holy city
B. a trading center
C. a seaport
D. an industrial center

5. In 1324, Mansu Musa made a long journey to Mecca.
He traveled from —

A. Greenland to Iceland
B. Europe to Asia
C. Europe to West Africa
D. West Africa to Arabia

6. Marco Polo learned about China by —

A. working for Kublai Khan and traveling throughout China
B. interviewing other Europeans who had been to China
C. studying Chinese literature, which described Chinese customs
D. interviewing Chinese who were exploring Europe

7. Marco Polo's book about China made Europeans feel —

A. disgusted by conditions in China
B. fearful of war with China
C. more interested in China
D. scornful of Chinese technology

8. For several centuries, Córdoba was Europe's largest city and its greatest center of learning mostly because —

A. it was the center of the Christian church
B. of its rich natural resources
C. Viking explorers used it as their base
D. of contact through trade with the Islamic world

Name ______________________ Date ______________

9. The drawing shows an astrolabe. What happened as a direct result of Europeans' use of the astrolabe?

A. More crops were produced.

B. New kinds of texts were published.

C. Voyages to new places became possible.

D. Larger, more impressive buildings could be built.

Choose a term from the list below that matches the description. Write the term in the space provided.

pilgrimage	**Islam**	**Renaissance**	**Arabic numeral**
merchant	**emperor**	**saga**	

10. the ruler of an empire

____

11. an ancient story of Iceland

____

12. a person who makes his or her living buying and selling goods

____

13. a journey to a sacred place

____

14. a belief in one God based on the teachings of the Prophet Mohammed

____

Name ______________________________ Date ____________________

Answer questions 15–20 in the spaces provided. Continue your answer on the back of the sheet if you need to.

15. Who was the leader of the first group of Europeans to explore North America?

____

16. West Africans traded gold for what product from North Africa?

____

17. When archaeologists found pieces of iron in L'Anse aux Meadows in Newfoundland, what conclusion did they draw?

____

____

____

18. How did Mansa Musa's pilgrimage to Mecca help make Timbuktu a center of learning and the arts?

____

____

____

19. What evidence supports the idea that China was the most advanced society in the world during the time of Kublai Khan?

____

____

20. Which ancient cultures helped inspire the rebirth of culture called the Renaissance?

____

Name ______________________________ Date ________________

You have learned about using media. Read the following paragraphs about a recent expedition to the North Pole. After reading the paragraphs, answer questions 21–23.

On Friday, April 21, 1995, a small team of Arctic researchers and explorers reached the North Pole. For them, the date of their arrival was important — it was Earth Day.

The crew had a special mission when they set out on their journey. They wanted to draw attention to the problem of increasing pollution of the Arctic environment. Air and water currents have been carrying pollutants into the Arctic from far away. They also wanted to share their adventures with students from around the world.

To help them achieve these goals, they used a computer to send messages to classrooms all across the nation. They sent messages from their computer to a satellite orbiting the pole, which relayed the message to a ground station. In fact, they were even able to send a picture from the North Pole over the Internet.

21. Write one sentence that summarizes the main idea of these paragraphs.

____

____

22. What opinion does the author have about pollution in the Arctic environment?

____

____

23. Think of a topic about pollution that interests you. Write the topic here.

____

In which media could you find information about your topic?
List TWO sources and what you could expect to find.

____

____

Name ______________________ Date ______________

Chapter 4 Test

Choose the best answer. Circle the letter next to your choice.

1. In the late fifteenth century, the Portuguese reached Asia by —

A. traveling overland through Europe to Asia Minor
B. sailing across the Mediterranean Sea to the Suez Canal
C. traveling overland across North Africa and Arabia
D. sailing around the African coast to the Indian Ocean

2. What land did Columbus hope to reach by sailing west from Spain?

A. North America
B. Asia
C. Central America
D. Australia

3. One reason that the Spanish defeated the Aztecs was that —

A. the Aztec empire lacked natural resources
B. Montezuma betrayed the Aztecs and fled with Spanish gold
C. the Aztec culture was a simple one
D. Montezuma, hoping for peace, invited the Spanish in

4. What did the explorers Pánfilo de Narváez and Francisco Coronado have in common?

A. Both searched unsuccessfully for the Seven Cities of Gold.
B. Both died brutal deaths in the deserts of the American Southwest.
C. Both used trickery to defeat the Aztecs.
D. Both took part in Magellan's effort to circumnavigate the globe.

5. Early in the sixteenth century, the Spanish brought enslaved Africans to the Americas. The Spanish forced these people to —

A. go to war against Native Americans
B. work on sugar plantations in the Caribbean
C. grow corn and other crops in Mexico
D. become sailors on Spanish and Portuguese ships

Name ____________________ Date ____________

6. Which of the following was present in the Americas before the arrival of Europeans?

A. cocoa
B. cows
C. wheat
D. smallpox

7. Why did Philip II of Spain want to fight the English?

A. He wanted to marry Queen Elizabeth I.
B. He hoped to prepare for war against France.
C. He was angry about English pirates like Drake.
D. He planned to capture Ireland.

8. How was Cartier's exploration of the St. Lawrence River similar to Hudson's exploration of the Hudson River?

A. Both men died when they were trapped by ice.
B. Both were trying to find the Northwest Passage.
C. Each started a settlement that became a major city.
D. Each found a route to the Pacific.

9. In the 1500s which of the following European countries was the MOST powerful?

A. England
B. Portugal
C. France
D. Spain

10. Which explorer made a voyage from England to Newfoundland?

A. Cabot
B. Drake
C. Magellan
D. Columbus

Name ______________________________ Date ________________

For questions 11-15, choose a word from the list below that fits the description. Write the word in the space provided.

armada **ambush** **slavery** **conquistador** **epidemic**
immunity **navigation** **settlement** **rebel**

11. a community of people in a new region ____________________

12. to resist authority ____________________

13. the spread of disease among many people ____________________

14. the science of plotting and controlling the course of a ship ____________________

15. a system in which people worked without pay and had no freedom ____________

Use the timeline to answer questions 16 and 17.

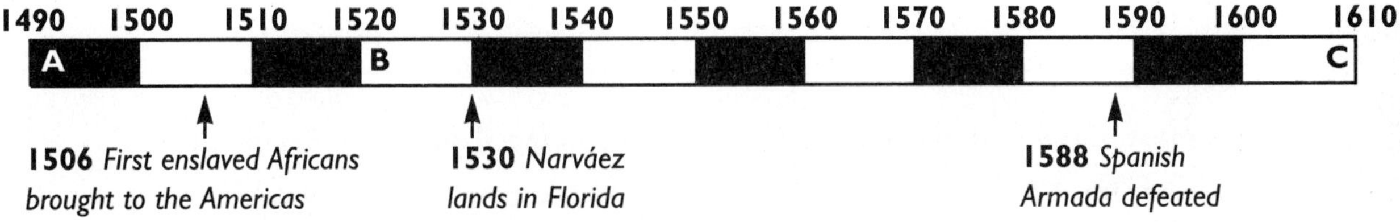

16. Which letter marks the year that Hudson claimed the Hudson River Valley for the Netherlands?

____

17. Which letter marks the year that Cortés defeated the Aztec Empire?

____

Answer questions 18-25 in the spaces provided. Continue your answer on the back of the sheet if you need to.

18. Would Portuguese sailors have been able to reach Asia in the fifteenth century if the compass had not been invented? Explain why or why not.

____

____

Name ______________________________ Date ______________

19. On each of Columbus' four voyages, he landed in places that were close to one another. What does this information tell you about the routes he took?

20. What evidence was there that the Seven Cities of Gold existed? Why do you think explorers kept looking for them?

21. How did the Columbian Exchange lead to the beginning of the African slave trade?

22. Most of the animals that were transferred in the Columbian Exchange went from Europe to the Americas. What is a good explanation for this?

23. This table shows the approximate population of central Mexico in 1500 and 1600. Give THREE reasons for the change in population.

Approximate Population of Mexico

in 1500	in 1600
25 million	1–2 million

Name ______________________ Date ______________

24. What was King Philip's purpose when he built the Spanish Armada?

____

____

25. Why did the French, the Dutch, and the English want to find the Northwest Passage?

____

____

Directions: Henry Hudson explored the river that is now named for him, the Hudson River. The map shows the location of the Hudson River. Use your map skills and your understanding of latitude and longitude to answer questions 26-29.

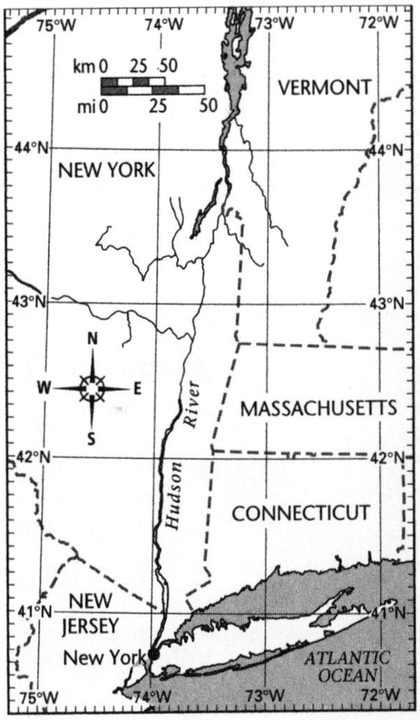

26. The Hudson River runs quite close to one line. What line is it?

____

27. What is the interval between longitude lines on this map?

____

28. What is the APPROXIMATE latitude and longitude where the Hudson River joins the Atlantic Ocean?

____

29. If a ship traveled up the Hudson through 30 minutes of latitude, about how many miles would it travel? How do you know?

____

____

Name ______________________________ Date ________________

Chapter 5 Test

Choose the best answer. Circle the letter next to your choice.

1. In the 1600s, what did MOST people in New Spain do for a living?

A. They were hunters and gatherers.

B. They were gold and silver miners.

C. They served as soldiers in the presidios.

D. They worked on haciendas.

2. What goal did the mission friars have concerning the religion of the Pueblo people?

A. They hoped to learn from it.

B. They thought it could exist side-by-side with Christianity.

C. They wanted to replace it with Christianity.

D. They planned to kill all those who practiced it.

3. What did John White find when he returned to the Roanoke colony after an absence of several years?

A. a busy settlement of fine farms

B. a handful of colonists, including his granddaughter

C. only a post with one word carved on it

D. no settlers, but a written record of the colony's problems

4. What was the goal of the founders of the Virginia Company?

A. to make a profit for London merchants

B. to introduce tobacco in Europe

C. to convert Native Americans to Christianity

D. to create a model Christian community

Name ______________________________ Date ______________

5. **The MAIN reason the Pilgrims left England was because they wanted to —**
   A. visit holy cities in the Middle East
   B. take high-paying jobs they had been promised in the Netherlands
   C. take advantage of the resources in America
   D. practice their religion in peace

6. **What was the goal of the Puritan leaders who ran Massachusetts Bay Colony?**
   A. to make money trading with Native Americans
   B. to make a profit by selling wood and other products
   C. to create a community that would be a model to the world
   D. to create an empire along the Atlantic Coast

7. **French colonists in New France made a living MOSTLY by —**
   A. creating large farms to export grain
   B. trapping and trading furs
   C. selling wood and other forest products
   D. settling on small farms

8. **How did the Dutch West India Company convince people to settle in New Netherland?**
   A. It sent missionaries to convert the Native Americans.
   B. It persecuted settlers for their religious beliefs.
   C. It granted large land areas to wealthy men.
   D. It built forts called presidios to protect settlers.

9. **Some settlers in the colonies tried to convert Native Americans to Catholicism. From which countries did they come?**
   A. England and the Netherlands
   B. France and Spain
   C. France and the Netherlands
   D. England and Spain

Name ______________________________ Date ________________

10. The shaded area on the map of North America in the seventeenth century shows land claimed by —

A. France
B. England
C. the Netherlands
D. Spain

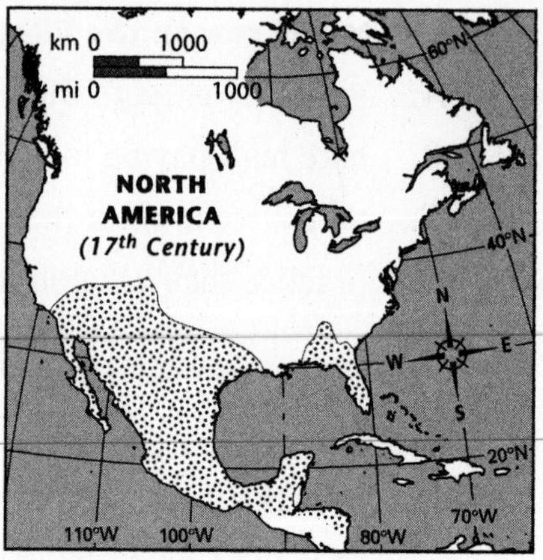

For questions 11–15, choose a word from the list below that matches the description. Write the word in the space provided.

Puritan	**patroon**	**viceroy**	**mestizo**	**missionary**
invest	**presidio**	**charter**	**colony**	**pelt**

11. an official document that gave a company the right to settle in North America

____

12. wealthy man who could afford to bring people and supplies to settle the land

____

13. a settlement ruled by a distant country

____

14. a person sent by a king to rule in his place

____

15. to give money to a company in return for stock

____

Name ______________________________ Date ________________

For questions 16 and 17, choose the letter on the map that best answers each question.

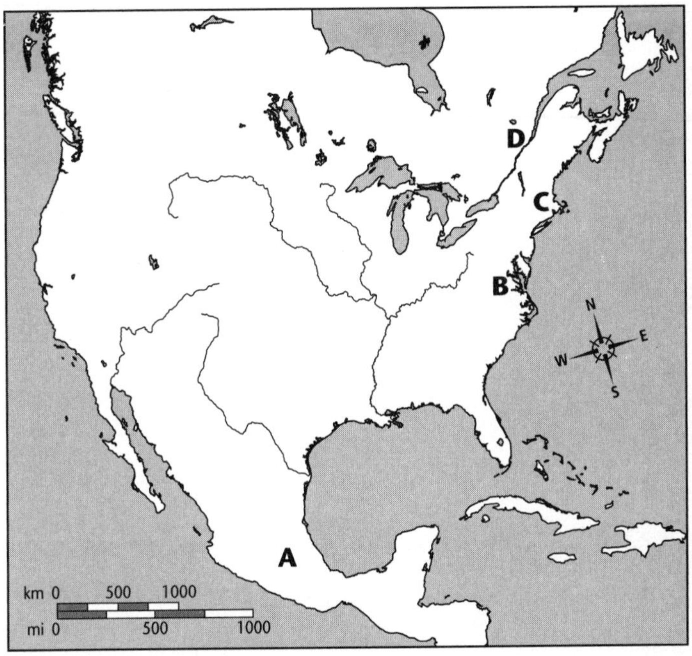

16. Which letter marks a fur-trading post in New France?

____

17. Which letter marks where the Pilgrims settled in 1620?

____

Answer questions 18–25 in the spaces provided. Continue your answer on the back of the sheet if you need to.

18. In New Spain, who did the hard work of tilling the soil? Why?

____

19. Why did the Pueblo people rebel against the Spanish?

____

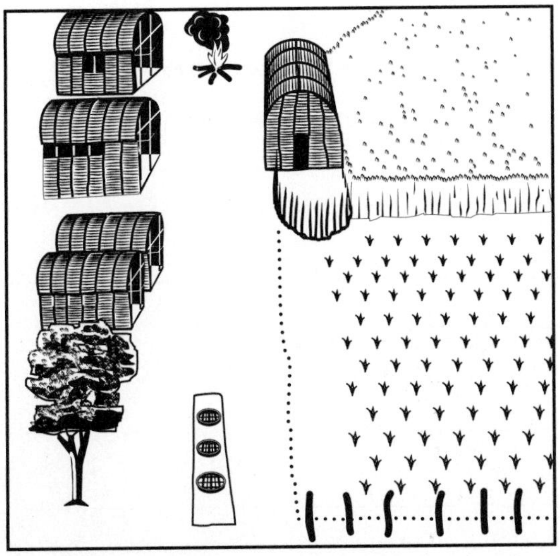

20. This picture is based on a sketch drawn by John White in 1685. What does it tell us about the lives of the Algonquin people?

____

____

____

____

Name ______________________ Date ______________

21. **If the tobacco seeds John Rolfe planted had not grown, how might the history of the Virginia colony have been different?**

____

22. **If students in a school today wanted to create their own document similar to the Mayflower Compact, what would it say?**

____

23. **Why was John Winthrop's leadership important to the growth of Boston?**

____

24. **How were the Jesuits in New France similar to the friars in New Spain?**

____

25. **Why were there people from many countries in New Amsterdam?**

____

Use what you have learned about primary and secondary sources to answer these questions. The following sentences are about Jamestown in 1609.

Sentence 1: The colonists expected that the Indians would provide them with corn, so they did not store enough of their own food for the winter.

Sentence 2: So lamentable was our scarcity, that we were constrained to eat dogs, cats, rats, snakes, toadstools, horsehides, and what not.

26. **Which sentence comes from a primary source? Which sentence comes from a secondary source? Explain how you decided which was which.**

____

____

27. **Identify a fact in sentence 2. How might you use it in a report?**

____

____

Name ______________________ Date ______________

Open-ended Response

In this unit you learned about explorers who took risks to learn something new. Use what you have learned to answer the following question.

Choose an explorer you have learned about, such as Marco Polo, Jacques Cartier, or Henry Hudson. What quality makes an explorer different from other people? How does your chosen explorer's life or voyage show this quality? You can express your answer by writing a poem, making a chart, or writing a paragraph.

Use the lines below for your notes. Prepare your response on separate sheets.

Theme Project Rubric

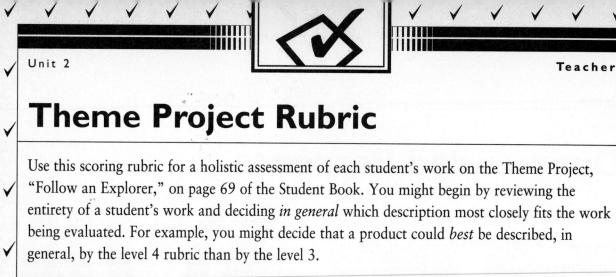

Use this scoring rubric for a holistic assessment of each student's work on the Theme Project, "Follow an Explorer," on page 69 of the Student Book. You might begin by reviewing the entirety of a student's work and deciding *in general* which description most closely fits the work being evaluated. For example, you might decide that a product could *best* be described, in general, by the level 4 rubric than by the level 3.

Level 4	Level 3	Level 2	Level 1
• The project demonstrates thorough and in-depth knowledge of a specific European explorer's encounters with new areas and peoples. • The project includes many of the following: a map, a costume or drawing, a story, and a collage. • The project clearly connects the concepts of exploration and encounter, analyzes routes and means of transportation, identifies the effects of weather and climate, and creatively extends these understandings. • Maps are clear and easily readable; writing is clear and well-organized; drawings and collages show planning and attention to detail. • The project reflects excellent application of map-making and research skills.	• The project demonstrates knowledge of a specific European explorer's encounters with new areas and peoples. • The project includes several types of work, such as a map, a costume or drawing, a collage, or a story. • The project connects the concepts of exploration and encounter, analyzes means of transportation, and includes only appropriate material. • The materials are mostly easy to read, are fairly well-organized, and have appropriate labels. • The project demonstrates map-making and research skills.	• The project shows some misunderstandings of European exploration and encounters with new areas and peoples. • The project includes only one or two types of work or some work that does not relate directly to the explorer selected. • The connection between exploration and encounter is not clarified. The project needs revising to identify routes, analyze means of transportation, connect climate and geography, and exclude inappropriate material. • The materials are difficult to read and are poorly organized. Titles and labels are missing or unclear. • The materials demonstrate distinct weaknesses in map-making and research skills.	• The project shows a fundamental misunderstanding of European exploration and encounters with new areas and peoples. • The work presented fails in significant ways to meet the assignment. • The connection between exploration and encounter is either not made or is illogical. There is little evidence of sound thinking skills. • The materials are difficult to read; no organization is evident. Maps and posters are missing or are not recognizable. • The materials provide little or no evidence of map-making or research skills.

Name ______________________________ Date ________________

Performance Assessment Event

Your teacher will give you directions for using this page.

In this unit, you have learned about exploration and encounter. If you could talk to an explorer whom you learned about in Unit 2, what would you like to know? Now you will have the chance to decide how to interview an explorer.

Choose a European explorer who came to America. Suppose you are going to interview this person on the radio. Since you will need to introduce this person to your audience, write notes for your introduction. Then write a list of ten specific questions you would ask.

Your interview preparation will be evaluated according to the following:

1. The introduction and interview questions show that you know about explorers in America.
2. The introduction gives a good picture of the explorer.
3. The interview questions ask for important information.
4. The questions are clear, specific, and logically organized.

Possible Extensions

A. With a classmate as a partner, conduct a pair of interviews. Take turns playing the roles of interviewer and explorer. Practice your interviews before you present them.

Your teacher and classmates will evaluate your pair of interviews based on the following criteria:

1. accuracy and completeness of information presented
2. style and organization of your presentation
3. equal participation of both partners

B. Make a tape recording of your interviews. Use sound effects, commercials, station identification, and other audio features to make the interviews sound as much like a radio program as possible.

Performance Assessment Tips

Performance Event

If your students have completed the Theme Project for Unit 2, encourage them to review the maps, drawings, stories, collages, and other materials they prepared. They should also look at their research about the people and climate along the explorer's route. Help students create a resource table to use for research on exploration and explorers. Possible resources include historical atlases, reference books, biographies of explorers, and books about Native American groups. Add material from theme projects.

The whole class can discuss exploration and explorers. Students could brainstorm a list of European explorers of the Americas and put the list on the board. Also, discuss what problems these explorers might have faced and what encounters they might have had.

Review the requirements of good interviews. Discuss in class how to introduce someone and how to ask good questions. As students write interview questions, have them work in pairs to see if the questions are interesting, specific, and understandable.

For work needing revision, provide clear directions. If notes are incomplete, suggest specific material that needs to be added. If questions are too vague, have students add more specifics. For students who must begin over, suggest that they may need to find out more about a particular explorer before writing the introduction or questions. Help students decide where they could find more information.

Extensions

A. Have students work in pairs to conduct interviews. Students should take turns playing the roles of interviewer and explorer to practice the interviews. Encourage students to use simple materials to create props and a costume for the explorer. They can then present the interviews to the class. One possible format—a radio talk show, in which other students in the class can "phone in" questions after the interview is finished.

B. Provide a tape recorder for students to use, and demonstrate how to use it. Suggest that students practice using the tape recorder to check whether their voices are clear and audible before they tape record the interviews. Also suggest that they carefully plan any audio effects in advance, making sure that they have any props required to create sound effects. These tapes could be included in portfolios to document the interviews.

Performance Assessment Rubric

Use this scoring rubric for a holistic assessment of each student's work on the Performance Assessment Event on page 33 of *Assessment Options*. You might begin by reviewing the entirety of a student's work and deciding *in general* which description most closely fits the work being evaluated. For example, you might decide that a product could *best* be described, in general, by the level 4 rubric rather than the level 3.

Level 4	Level 3	Level 2	Level 1
• The introduction notes and interview questions demonstrate an outstanding knowledge of exploration in America and a sense of the personality and accomplishments of the explorer. • The notes are complete, and the questions are detailed and specific. • The material is logically organized. The introduction and questions concentrate on important topics. • The notes and questions can be easily understood by an interviewee and audience. • The materials reflect excellent application of such social studies skills as interviewing skills, using source materials, and organizing information.	• The notes and questions demonstrate satisfactory knowledge of exploration in America. • Notes cover main points, and most questions are specific. • Most material is logically organized and focuses on important topics. • The material is generally clear and most of it can be easily understood. • The student has applied social studies skills such as interviewing skills, using source materials, and organizing material.	• The notes and questions demonstrate some knowledge of exploration in America. There are some errors or omissions in content. • Notes give some information about the explorer, but not an adequate one; some questions are on target, but there are too few or some are too general. • The material lacks clear organization; some parts are off the topic or trivial. • Parts of the notes and questions are unclear. • The student shows only fair or incomplete application of social studies skills such as interviewing skills, using source materials, and organizing material.	• The notes and questions do not indicate an understanding of the exploration of America. • Notes are uninformative; the questions are too few and too vague. • The materials are not logically presented and show little or no evidence of sound thinking skills. • The materials are unclear. • The materials show little evidence of the use of social studies skills.

Name ______________________________ Date ______________

Chapter 6 Test

Choose the best answer. Circle the letter next to your choice.

1. The MOST abundant natural resource in the New England colonies was —

A. rich soil
B. maple syrup
C. iron
D. wood

2. Why did the first Pilgrim colonists find much of the cleared land abandoned?

A. The Native Americans who cleared it had died from diseases.
B. The early explorers had farmed it and then moved westward.
C. Native Americans had cleared it to welcome the settlers.
D. Fierce storms, not human activity, had cleared the land.

3. When Puritans planned their communities, they tried to make sure that —

A. everyone had the same amount of land
B. people of all religions were welcome
C. the communities could provide for all their own needs
D. women had an equal share in decision making

4. The MAIN goal of Puritan education was to make sure all children —

A. would enjoy reading stories and poems
B. could understand religious readings
C. would be able to go to college
D. could add and subtract amounts of money

5. What did Roger Williams and Anne Hutchinson have in common?

A. Both were banished for being dissenters.
B. Together they founded the colony of Connecticut.
C. Both were New Lights who preached fiery sermons.
D. Both were accused during the Salem witch trials.

Name ________________________________ Date ____________________

6. **What did the Salem witch trials show about the relationship between townspeople in the town of Salem?**
   A. Ministers told people how to help one another.
   B. Neighbors distrusted one another.
   C. As the community grew larger, people became closer.
   D. People in the community cared more about money than religion.

7. **Why were the Puritans who came after 1630 unable to enjoy peace with the Native Americans, as the Pilgrims had before?**
   A. There were many more Puritans than Pilgrims, and they wanted more land.
   B. The Puritans tried to convert the Native Americans to Christianity.
   C. Native Americans disliked the goods the Puritans used for trade.
   D. After 1630 the Puritans tried to enslave Native Americans.

8. **Where was King Phillip's War fought in 1675?**
   A. mainly in Boston
   B. all over New England
   C. in areas controlled by the Pequot people
   D. along the seacoast in places like Mystic, Connecticut.

9. **Which of the following items was imported rather than made by a New England farm family?**
   A. clothes
   B. guns
   C. candles
   D. maple syrup

10. **In Puritan villages, what work did children typically do?**
   A. They worked at the meetinghouse for the public good.
   B. Their only job was to study well in school.
   C. They worked in small mills and factories.
   D. They worked long days at home and in the fields.

Name ______________________ Date ______________

11. What happened to the fish caught in New England?

A. They were used only to feed seaside villages.
B. They were traded with other colonies for manufactured goods.
C. They were used at home, and traded to other countries.
D. They were turned into fertilizer and used on farms.

12. Where did the New England colonies get the ships they used in fishing and trade?

A. They bought their ships from England.
B. They made their ships in local shipyards.
C. They bought their ships from the Middle Colonies.
D. They rented ships from English merchants.

For questions 13–17, choose the term from the list below that matches the description. Write the term in the space provided.

wampum	**cod**	**meetinghouse**	**imports**
triangular trade	**dissenters**	**self-sufficient**	**wilderness**

13. the Native American money made of polished shells

____

14. providing for one's own needs ______________________

15. route between Africa, Europe, and North America

____

16. the building at the center of Puritan life ______________________

17. items bought from distant places ______________________

Name ______________________ Date ______________

Use the map to answer questions 18 and 19.

18. Mark the location of Boston.

19. Mark the location of Rhode Island.

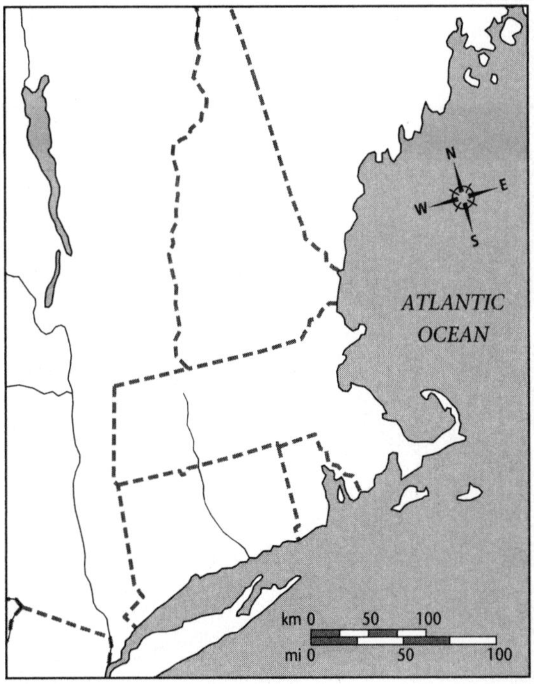

Answer questions 20–25 in the spaces provided. Continue your answer on the back of the sheet if you need to.

20. Why wasn't New England's land well-suited for farming?

____

21. How was land divided among families in a Puritan village? Was this fair or unfair? Explain your answer.

____

____

22. How did the words and actions of people like Williams, Hutchinson, and Edwards bring new forms of faith to New England?

____

23. What was King Philip's War? What was the outcome?

____

24. How did the daily work of children in the New England colonies differ from the work children do today?

____

Name ______________________ Date ______________

25. What economic activities made Boston the richest city in the colonies by 1700?

____

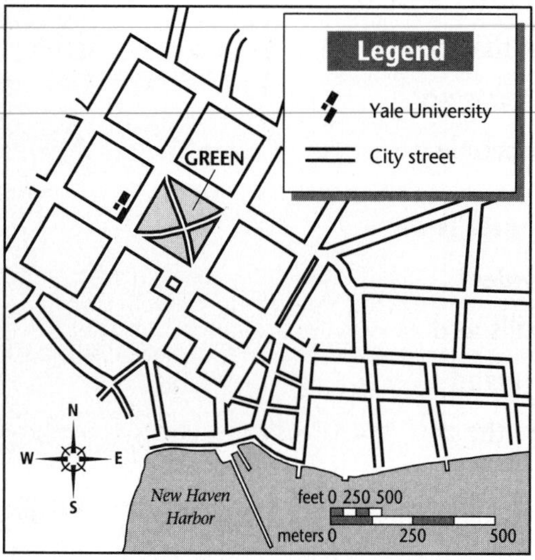

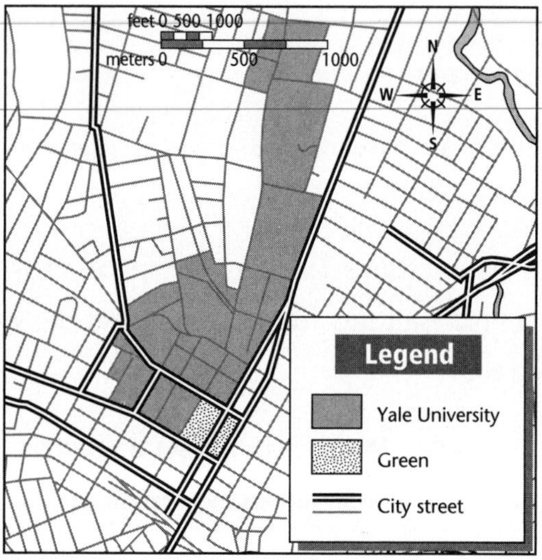

You have learned about reading maps to see change over time. The two maps below show New Haven, Connecticut. The map on the left shows the city in 1775, and the map on the right shows it today. Use the maps and your map skills to answer questions 26–28.

26. What feature on the 1775 map is about the SAME on the map today?

____

27. How does the size of Yale University today compare with its size in 1775?

____

28. How does the grid pattern of the streets today compare to the way it was in 1775?

____

Name ______________________ Date ______________

Chapter 7 Test

Choose the best answer. Circle the letter next to your choice.

1. How did the Ice Age glaciers benefit the Middle Colonies?

A. by making the growing season longer so there was more sunlight
B. by bulldozing the roots away so that people could plant
C. by depositing fertile topsoil that was good for farming
D. by leaving deposits of gravel so people could build roads

2. What was one major effect the waterfalls caused by the fall line had on the Middle Colonies?

A. They provided power for sawmills and gristmills.
B. They connected the coast with inland towns.
C. They made it possible to irrigate the land for farming.
D. They acted as a boundary for settlements.

3. New York and New Jersey were called proprietary colonies. What was the MAIN goal of their proprietors?

A. to sell supplies to the colonists
B. to create model democratic communities
C. to build port cities that would lead to rich trade
D. to make money by renting land to the colonists

4. How were the beliefs of Pennsylvania Quakers different from the beliefs of Puritans?

A. Unlike Puritans, Quakers believed that everyone in their colony should be a Quaker.
B. Unlike Quakers, Puritans believed that only their own religion should be practiced.
C. Unlike Puritans, Quakers wanted to learn the religion of the Lenni Lenape.
D. Unlike Quakers, Puritans believed in toleration of all religions.

Name ______________________________ Date ________________

5. The New England colonies were mostly settled by people from England. Which statement BEST describes those who moved to the Middle Colonies?

A. They were from England.
B. They were from Germany.
C. They were from Scotland.
D. They came from many different countries.

6. By 1740, enslaved people made up between ten and fifteen percent of the population of the Middle Colonies. Where did MOST of these people live?

A. in the countryside in Pennsylvania
B. beyond the fall line on yeoman farms
C. in the cities of New York and Philadelphia
D. They were evenly spread throughout the colonies.

7. What product was produced in the fields of the settled areas of the "Breadbasket Colonies"?

A. the subsistence crops needed to survive
B. dairy products to trade for other regions' bread
C. grain crops such as wheat, corn, and barley
D. chickens, cows, and pigs for meat

8. The MAIN reason that land was cheaper in the backcountry was that it —

A. often suffered from flooding
B. was far from the markets of the city
C. was owned by church groups
D. provided rich crops with less work

9. What was one way that New York and Philadelphia were alike?

A. both were planned cities
B. both had straight, wide avenues
C. both had harbors that were good for shipping
D. both suffered from a poor climate

Name ______________________ Date ______________

10. What made Philadelphia different from most colonial cities?

A. It was protected by a thick wall.
B. Its economy was based entirely on trade.
C. It had a poor location.
D. It was based on a plan.

For questions 11–15, choose the term from the list below that matches the description. Write the term in the space provided.

fall line	**subsistence**	**religious toleration**
holy experiment	**backcountry**	**proprietor**
apprentice	**yeoman**	**Piedmont**

11. raising just enough food to survive upon ______________

12. a self-sufficient farmer who owned his own land ______________

13. the unsettled or wilderness part of each colony, usually beyond the fall line

____

14. a region of rolling hills ______________

15. a person who works with an older, experienced person to learn a skill

____

Answer questions 16 and 17 in the spaces provided.

16. When the English captured New Netherlands, New Amsterdam became

____

17. What city is known as "The City of Brotherly Love"? ______________

Name ______________________ Date ______________

Use the map to answer questions 18 and 19.

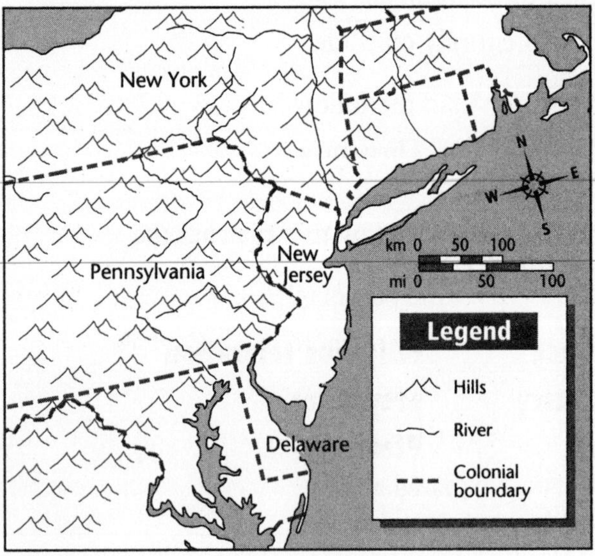

18. Label the location of the Delaware River.

19. Draw a line showing the location of the fall line.

Answer questions 20–24 in the spaces provided. Continue your answer on the back of the sheet if you need to.

20. Explain what effect the waterfalls had on the Middle Colonies' development.

____

21. How do the names of Pennsylvania and New York reflect their origins?

____

22. When William Penn advertised for settlers, what kinds of people were attracted to Pennsylvania and why?

____

____

23. What happened to wheat grown in settled areas of the Middle Colonies?

____

Name ______________________________ Date ________________

24. Penn planned his city carefully. Describe TWO features that illustrate this.

____

Look for cause-and-effect relationships as you read the following passage from a diary kept by Samuel Sewall, a colonist in Boston. Then answer questions 25–28.

from the Diary of Samuel Sewall

April 29, 1695. The morning is very warm and Sunshiny; in the Afternoon there is Thunder and Lightening, and about 2 P.M. a very extraordinary Storm of Hail, so that the ground was made white with it, as with the blossoms when fallen; 'twas as bigg as pistoll and Musquet Bullets; It broke of the Glass of the New House about 480 Quarrels [panes] of the Front . . . People afterward Gazed about the House to see its Ruins.

25. What event is Samuel Sewall describing?

____

26. What caused the ground to become completely white?

____

27. What clue word or words help you find the effect of the storm?

____

28. Fill in the cause-and-effect chart to show TWO effects of the storm.

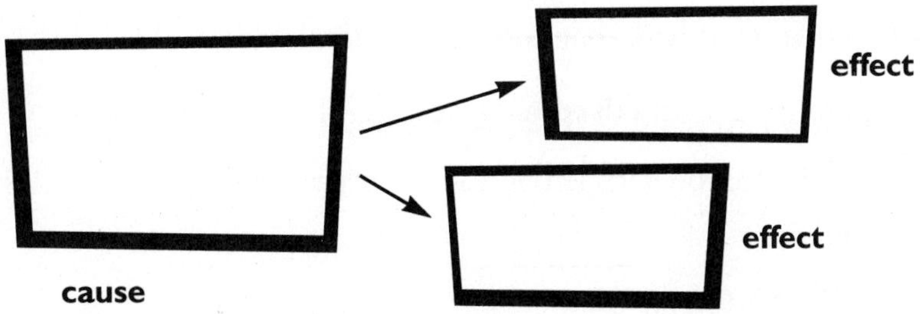

Name ______________________ Date ______________

Chapter 8 Test

Choose the best answer. Circle the letter next to your choice.

1. What was one reason that farmers in the Southern Colonies were able to grow cash crops?

A. They had a long growing season.

B. They imported their food from the Northern Colonies.

C. They traded with Native Americans for most goods.

D. There were large cities in the South that needed these crops.

2. How did the rivers of the tidewater region affect agriculture?

A. Crops were frequently flooded and destroyed.

B. People could easily ship their crops along rivers.

C. In the dry climate river water was required for any farming.

D. The soil was too wet and soggy for successful farming.

3. What was the MAIN reason that tobacco planters in Virginia and Maryland invaded Native American territory?

A. Their own land was not suited to growing tobacco.

B. Native American lands were closer to major trade routes.

C. Tobacco farming required much land.

D. Native Americans had abandoned the land already.

4. In what way was Maryland settled like Virginia?

A. Large plantation owners settled the tidewater region, with small farmers in the interior.

B. Most settlers were Puritans.

C. The settlers were just released from English prisons.

D. Many settlers had little agricultural experience.

Name ______________________ Date ______________

5. Which industry was strongest in colonial North Carolina?

A. manufacturing metal products

B. indigo plantations

C. forest products

D. fish and ocean products

6. Georgia has been called "the most unusual" colony. The ideas used to settle Georgia came from —

A. Lord Baltimore

B. Nathaniel Bacon

C. Eliza Lucas

D. James Oglethorpe

7. The post road from Maine to Georgia was built so that —

A. a system of inns could be created

B. the mail could get through

C. debtors could be employed

D. trade between Northern and Southern Colonies could grow

8. Compared with the Northern Colonies, the cities in the Southern Colonies were —

A. richer and more diverse

B. fewer and smaller

C. about the same area and population

D. about the same area but with a larger population

9. How were MOST small farmers in the Southern Colonies different from plantation owners?

A. They grew only crops for sale.

B. They did not need to be self-sufficient.

C. They lived closer to the ports.

D. They did not own slaves.

Name ______________________________ Date ________________

10. Where were most of the enslaved Africans in the South living in 1775?

A. In North Carolina and Georgia

B. Along the coast of all the Southern colonies

C. In South Carolina and Virginia

D. In South Carolina and North Carolina

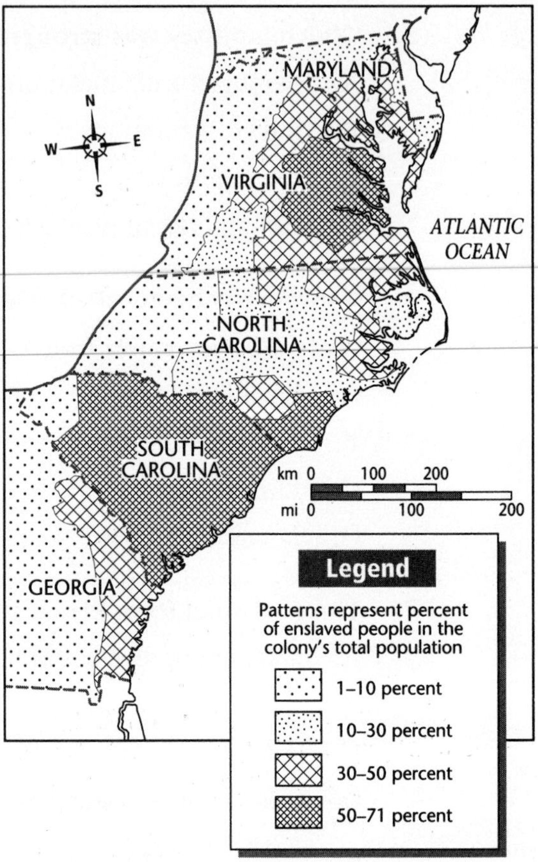

For questions 11–15, choose the term that best matches the description. Write the term in the space provided.

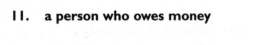

trustee	**representative**	**House of Burgesses**
debtor	**post road**	**tidewater**
export	**profit**	**cash crop**

11. a person who owes money

____

12. the coastal area where rivers are affected by ocean tides

____

13. goods shipped to another country to be sold

____

14. a person who speaks for other people

____

15. extra money after expenses have been paid

____

Name ______________________________ Date ________________

Answer questions 16–22 in the spaces provided. Continue your answer on the back of the sheet if you need to.

16. **What crop was grown in all parts of the south and used MAINLY to feed the colonists and their animals?**

____

17. **Which colony was founded for Catholic settlers and promised tolerance of other religions?**

____

18. **If you were a planter in South Carolina in 1750, which crop would you grow to make a living, indigo or corn? Explain your decision.**

____

____

19. **What group of farmers did the House of Burgesses favor when writing laws? Explain why this was so.**

____

____

20. **Why was it harder to make a living in the colony of North Carolina than in the colony of South Carolina?**

____

21. **What role did inns have in the rural South?**

____

22. **Why were plantations more profitable than yeoman farms?**

____

____

Name ______________________________ Date ________________

The map shows English migration from 1630 to 1660. Use your map skills and the map to answer questions 23–25.

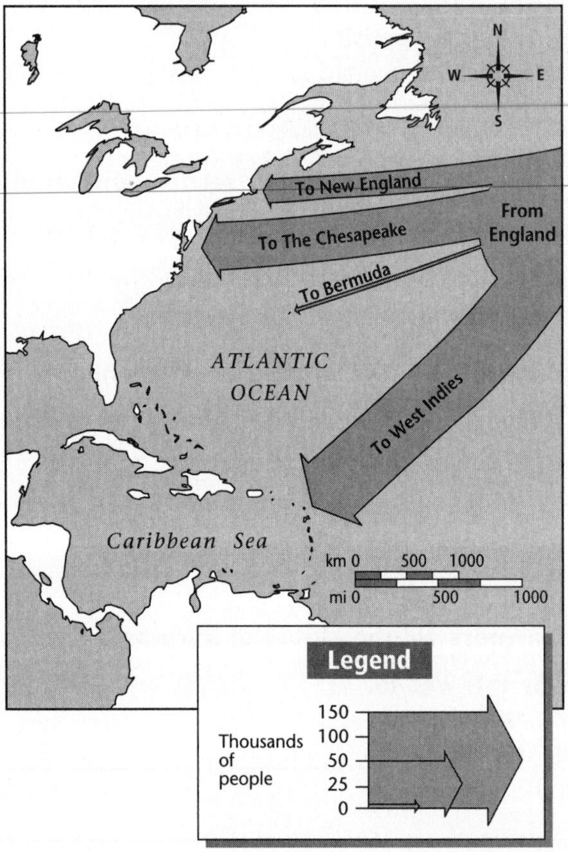

23. Which arrow is the thickest? What does this mean?

____

24. What does the arrow tell you about the direction in which people moved?

____

25. Compare the number of people moving to the Chesapeake and the number moving to New England.

____

Name ____________________ Date ____________

Open-ended Response

In this unit, you have learned how European colonists began to settle in New England, the Middle Colonies, and the South. The map shows the colonies in the early 1700s.

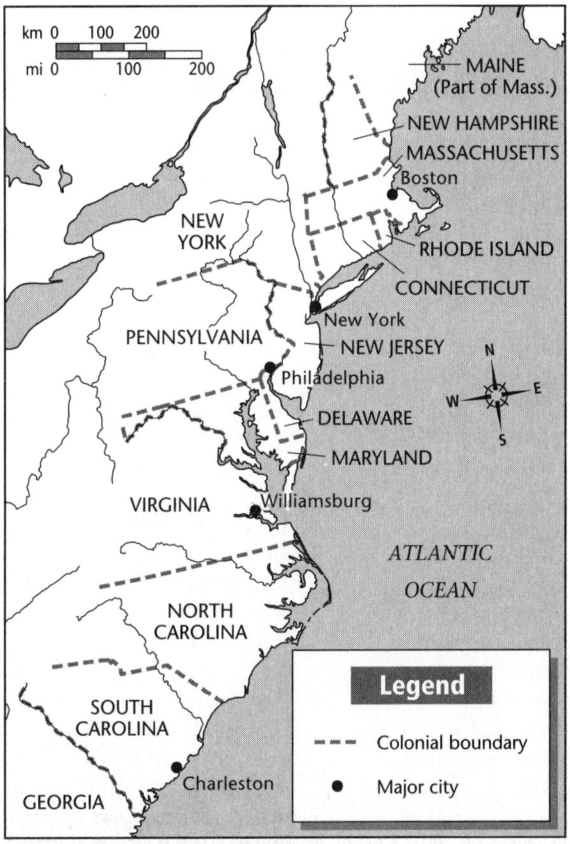

Suppose you were a European immigrant who decided to migrate to one of these colonies in the early 1700s. Which colony would you have chosen to settle in? Explain why. Use what you learned in the unit to justify your answer. Your answer may be in the form of a list of advantages, a labeled drawing showing the good features of your choice, a paragraph explaining your reasons, or a flyer that invites people to settle in this colony.

Use the space below for your notes. Prepare your response on separate sheets.

____

____

Theme Project Rubric

Use this scoring rubric for a holistic assessment of each student's work on the Theme Project "Come to America!" on page 155 of the Student Book. You might begin by reviewing the entirety of a student's work and deciding *in general* which description most closely fits the work being evaluated. For example, you might decide that a product could *best* be described, in general, by the level 4 rubric than by the level 3.

Level 4	Level 3	Level 2	Level 1
• The brochure demonstrates thorough and in-depth knowledge of how the colonists adjusted to the native people and geography of the East Coast. • The brochure includes many of the following: a map, drawings, descriptions, and explanations. • The brochure analyzes geographic features and social attitudes and customs, evaluates and synthesizes a variety of facts, and builds to a logical conclusion. • Maps are clear and easily readable, writing is clear and well-organized, drawings show evidence of planning and attention to detail. • The brochure reflects excellent application of map making and research skills.	• The brochure demonstrates knowledge of how colonists lived in the colonies in the late 17th century. • The brochure includes several pieces of work, such as maps, drawings, and written descriptions. • The brochure is mostly designed for a persuasive purpose. The brochure includes analysis and evaluation and leads to a logical conclusion. • The brochure is mostly easy to read and well-organized. Materials have appropriate titles and labels. • The brochure reflects use of appropriate map making and research skills.	• The brochure demonstrates misunderstandings of how colonists lived in the colonies in the late 17th century. • The brochure includes only one or two types of work or some work that does not relate directly to the region, the time period, or how the colonists adjusted to their new environment. • The persuasive purpose of the brochure is not clear. The brochure needs revising to identify relationships, analyze causes, and exclude inappropriate materials. • The brochure is difficult to read and needs to be better organized. Titles and labels are missing or unclear. • The brochure demonstrates distinct weaknesses in map making and research skills.	• The brochure shows a fundamental misunderstanding of the native people and the geography of the east coast of North America in the late 17th century. • The brochure fails in significant ways to meet the assignment. • The purpose of the brochure is unclear. There is little evidence of sound thinking skills. • The materials are difficult to read; no organization is apparent. Map is missing or features are not recognizable. • The materials provide little or no evidence of map making or research skills.

Name ______________________ Date ______________

Performance Assessment Event

Your teacher will give you directions for using this page.

In this unit, you have learned about how European colonists adjusted to new environments in New England, the Middle Colonies, and the South. In these new environments, the colonists met new people and found new landscapes. They ate new foods such as corn and saw animals unknown in Europe.

Suppose you are one of these colonists. You have seen much that amazes you. You are living in ways very different from those in your homeland. Perhaps you are enjoying new freedom; perhaps you are feeling homesick.

As a colonist, write a letter to a friend or relative you have left behind. Describe what you are seeing and feeling. Be sure your letter explains what is different in your new environment. You can include sketches in your letter if you want. Attach to your letter a brief description of the colonist who wrote the letter.

Here is what your teacher will look for in evaluating your letter:

1. Does your letter show that you know a lot about the colony and the time period in which your letter writer lived?
2. Does the letter include a lot of descriptive, specific detail about the colony — and the letter writer?
3. Do you compare the writer's old and new environments?
4. Is it clear whom the letter is being sent to — who your audience is?

Possible Extensions

A. Put the letters from the class into a box. Take one letter from the box and answer it. In your letter, respond to the descriptions of colonial life. Include news from home and ask questions about life in the colonies. Then find the person who wrote the original letter. Work together to create a dialogue you can present to the class.

Dialogue will be evaluated according to the following criteria:

1. accurate and interesting details
2. style and organization of your presentation
3. equal participation of both partners

B. Think about what might happen to your colonist during the course of a year. Write diary entries that reflect both the events of the year and the colonist's reactions to those events.

Performance Assessment Tips

Performance Event

If your students have completed the Theme Project for Unit 3, encourage them to review the brochures they made and the pictures they drew. They should also look at their research about a details of daily life in the colonies.

Suggest that students consider how life in the new environment differed from life in the old environment. Students can brainstorm differences and list them on the board. It might be helpful to make separate lists for different regions in the colonies, indicating common and unique aspects. Individual students might then create a comparison chart that shows the differences in the old and new environments of the colonist they have chosen.

Review the requirements of writing a letter. Point out the kinds of descriptive details that make letters fun and interesting to read. Remind students that personal letters offer the opportunity to express feelings. Have students read some good letters as models.

Help students create a resource table to use in writing letters. Possible resources include research accounts, reference books, and books of artwork and photographs. Add material from theme projects if your students have done these projects.

You might check drafts of students' letters. For work needing revision, point out the major problem(s) in the student's work. Let the student suggest a strategy for fixing the problem.

Extensions

A. Before they begin writing responses to the letters, have students note the points they would like to make. They might use the following questions to get themselves started.

- Remember that you are living in the country from which the colonist came. How might your attitudes and life be different from the colonist's? Would this make you react strongly to anything in the letter?
- What subjects in the letter would you want to know more about?
- What would the colonist like to know more about? Share news about the colonist's home country.

B. Before students begin their diaries, have them create a rough timeline of events that the colonist might experience during one year. Remind students to keep the seasons in mind and to choose events appropriate to the time of year. For example, a colonial child living in North Carolina would probably not take part in a snowball fight in April.

Performance Assessment Rubric

Use this scoring rubric for a holistic assessment of each student's work on the Performance Assessment Event on page 53 of Assessment Options. You might begin by reviewing the entirety of a student's work and deciding *in general* which description most closely fits the work being evaluated. For example, you might decide that a product could *best* be described, in general, by the level 4 rubric rather than the level 3.

Level 4	Level 3	Level 2	Level 1
• The letter demonstrates an outstanding knowledge of conditions in a specific colony and general knowledge of the historical period. • The letter contains detailed, precise descriptive information. The colonist is clearly identified, with recognizable values, beliefs, and personal attributes. • The letter clearly compares the old and new environments and presents specific examples from the new environment. The letter shows creative thinking. • The letter is appropriately written for its audience, with his or her own identity. • The letter reflects excellent application of such social studies skills as using source materials, role-playing, and having historical perspective.	• The letter demonstrates a good knowledge of a specific colony and the historical period. • Descriptive material is included. The colonist is clearly identified, but without much sense of his or her personality. • The letter contains a comparison that is supported with some detail. • The letter is appropriate for its audience, but there is little sense of the recipient's individuality. • The student has applied some social studies skills such as using source materials, role-playing, and having historical perspective.	• The letter demonstrates some knowledge of colonial life, but there are some omissions. • Descriptive material is weak. There is no sense of the letter writer's attitudes or individuality. • Some points of comparison are made, but weakly and with some inaccuracies. The comparison is supported with few specific details. • Parts of the letter are not appropriate for its audience. • The letter demonstrates little evidence of social studies skills.	• The letter shows a lack of understanding of the colonial period. • Several sections of the assignment are omitted. • The letter shows little or no evidence of sound comparison. The material presented is weakly organized or illogical. • The letter is inappropriate for its audience. • The letter does not show evidence that the student used social studies skills to write it.

Name ______________________ Date ______________

Chapter 9 Test

Choose the best answer. Circle the letter next to your choice.

1. In the early 1750s, the Ohio River Valley was a center of conflict because BOTH the French and the British wanted to —

A. farm the rich lands
B. ship crops on the river
C. profit from the fur trade
D. sell manufactured goods there

2. When Benjamin Franklin proposed the Albany Plan of Union, he wanted the colonies to —

A. join together to fight the French
B. make George Washington their military leader
C. declare independence from Britain
D. protest the Proclamation of 1763

3. What was the relationship between Pontiac's Rebellion and the Proclamation of 1763?

A. The rebellion led the British to issue the proclamation.
B. The rebellion happened because the British issued the proclamation.
C. The rebellion and the proclamation were both causes of the French and Indian War.
D. Although the rebellion happened just before the proclamation, the two were not related.

Name ______________________ Date ______________

4. What happened as a result of the French and Indian War?

A. Many Native Americans moved to New France.

B. France lost all land claims in North America.

C. Britain was forced to abandon its claims in North America.

D. France expanded the area it controlled in North America.

5. In 1765, the British Parliament passed a tax on the colonies. The tax was intended to pay for —

A. British troops protecting the American colonists during the war

B. British troops fighting the French in Europe

C. the cost of protecting mail sent in the colonies

D. the coronation ceremonies of King George III

6. Why were the Sons of Liberty formed?

A. to help pay British war debts

B. to train colonists to be stamp agents

C. to settle in former French colonies

D. to encourage colonists to defy the Stamp Act

7. What was one way the colonists protested the Townshend Act?

A. They shot and killed British tax collectors.

B. They boycotted British-made goods.

C. They wrote to their representatives in the British Parliament.

D. They moved to major colonial cities.

8. What finally happened to the Townshend Acts?

A. They were all repealed by Parliament.

B. King George III said the colonists could ignore the acts.

C. Parliament repealed all the taxes except the one on tea.

D. The duties called for in the Acts were reduced.

Name ______________________________ Date ________________

For questions 9-13, choose a word from the list below that matches the description. Write the word in the space provided.

congress	**boycott**	**ally**	**Parliament**
duty	**repeal**	**proclamation**	

9. a meeting of representatives ______________________

10. a tax on imported goods ______________________

11. refusal to buy a product or service, or to deal with a business, or nation, as a means of protest

____

12. a person who joins with others for a specific purpose ______________________

13. an official announcement ______________________

Answer questions 14-19 in the spaces provided. Continue your answer on the back of the sheet if you need to.

14. Who won the French and Indian War? ______________________

15. What types of products were taxed under the Townshend Acts?

____

16. In 1754, representatives from seven colonies met with Iroquois chiefs. What did the colonists hope to persuade the Iroquois to do?

____

____

Name ______________________ Date ______________

17. Identify the line shown on this map of 1763, and explain its importance.

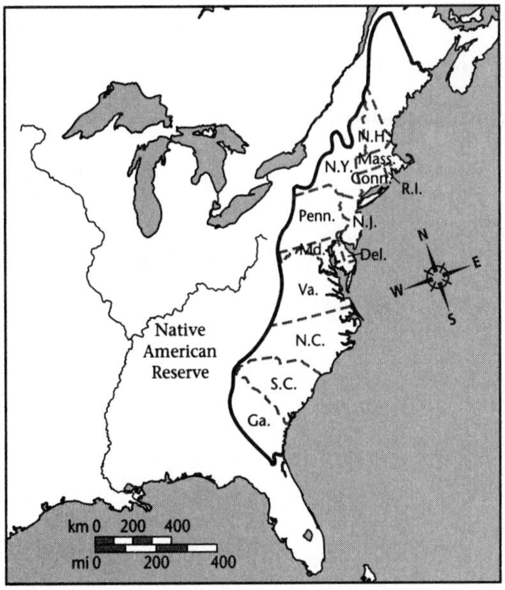

____

____

____

____

18. What products did the Stamp Act tax? ______________________

____

19. What evidence shows that the boycott was an effective way to protest the Townshend Acts?

____

____

____

Name ______________________________ Date ____________________

The map shows Montcalm's headquarters and his route to the Battle of Québec on the Plains of Abraham. Use what you have learned about reading battle maps to answer questions 20-22.

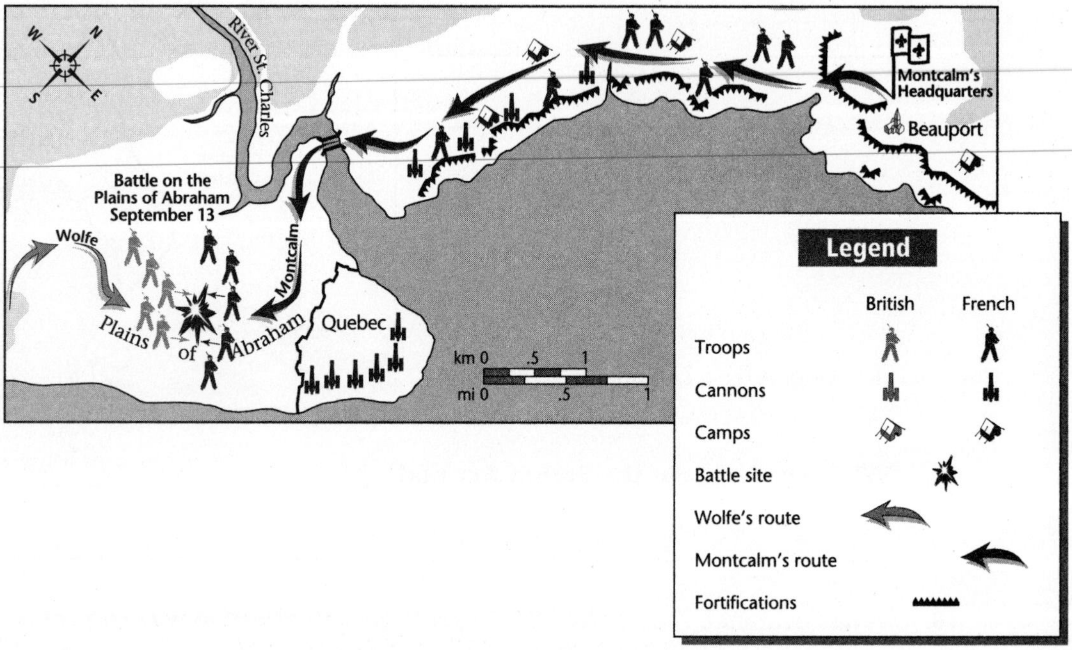

20. Were Montcalm's headquarters well protected? Explain.

____

21. Describe Montcalm's route to the Plains of Abraham.

____

____

22. Could the British have attacked Montcalm along his route to the River St. Charles? Explain why this would or would not have been a good idea.

____

____

Name ______________________ Date ______________

Chapter 10 Test

Choose the best answer. Circle the letter next to your choice.

1. **On March 5, 1770, British soldiers fired on colonists in Boston. Why did the soldiers fire?**
   A. The colonists had tried to steal their horses.
   B. The colonists had already shot at them.
   C. Britain was at war with the colonies.
   D. They feared for their safety.

2. **The colonists called the events of March 5, 1770, "a massacre." Why did they use this term?**
   A. to gain public support for their side
   B. to be accurate about what happened
   C. to make fun of the British soldiers
   D. to blame Native Americans for the event

3. **How did MOST colonists react to the Tea Act?**
   A. They were pleased to be able to buy tea again.
   B. They bought their tea from French merchants.
   C. They were angry and refused to buy tea.
   D. They made peace with Britain.

4. **If you had been a Loyalist, how would you probably have reacted to the passage of the Intolerable Acts?**
   A. by writing to a committee of correspondence
   B. by supporting Britain's demonstration of its authority
   C. by sending food and supplies to Boston
   D. by criticizing Parliament and the King

Name ______________________________ Date ____________________

5. What role did Paul Revere and William Dawes play in the battles of Lexington and Concord?

A. They were the first men killed by the British.

B. Revere led the Minutemen in Lexington, and Dawes led them in Concord.

C. They rode out to warn people that the British were coming.

D. Their drawings of the battles shaped public opinion.

6. What happened to British troops marching back to Boston after the battle in Concord?

A. They found the Minutemen's store of weapons.

B. They burned down houses in the surrounding towns.

C. Hidden Minutemen shot at them.

D. Local people cheered for them.

7. At the Second Continental Congress, the delegates agreed to —

A. fight the British at Bunker Hill

B. send an army to help the Boston Patriots

C. declare the colonies' independence from Britain

D. elect George Washington as the President

8. In what way could Americans claim they won the Battle of Bunker Hill?

A. They forced King George to loosen control of the colonies.

B. They kept control of both Bunker Hill and Breed's Hill.

C. They proved their training and equipment were better than Britain's.

D. They fought well and caused many British casualties.

9. What was the purpose of the Olive Branch Petition?

A. to declare independence of Britain

B. to apologize for the killing of British troops in Massachusetts

C. to seek a peaceful agreement with King George

D. to ask other colonies for help

Name ______________________________ Date ________________

10. Which of the following quotations most likely comes from Thomas Paine's *Common Sense*?

A. "We have it in our power to begin the world over again."
B. "We hold these truths to be self-evident, that all men are created equal."
C. "Don't one of you fire until you see the whites of their eyes."
D. "The town of Boston ought to be knocked about by the ears and destroy'd."

11. Why were the signers of the Declaration of Independence guilty of treason?

A. They were not representing the opinion of the colonists.
B. They were revolting against the British government.
C. They had signed the document without reading it first.
D. They did not have the support of Congress.

12. What was the main purpose of the Declaration of Independence?

A. to declare war on Britain
B. to state that each colony was independent of the other colonies
C. to repeal the Townshend Acts
D. to say that the colonies were free of British rule

For questions 13-17, choose a word from the list below that matches the description. Write the word in the space provided.

peninsula	**fortify**	**delegate**	**casualty**	**petition**
militia	**propaganda**	**Loyalist**	**Patriot**	**declaration**

13. information used to win support for a cause ____________________

14. a written request signed by many people ____________________

15. an army made up of ordinary citizens ____________________

16. a piece of land that juts out into a body of water ____________________

17. a person chosen to represent a group of people ____________________

Name ______________________________ Date ____________________

Answer questions 18-25 in the spaces provided. Continue your answer on the back of the sheet if you need to.

18. When was the Declaration of Independence signed? ____________________

19. Who wrote the Declaration of Independence? ____________________

20. How did colonists react to the Boston Massacre?

____

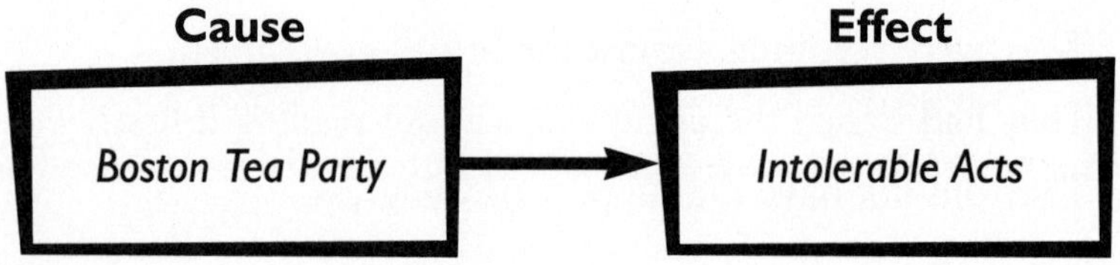

21. The boxes show the relationship between the Boston Tea Party and the Intolerable Acts. Explain why the cause led to the effect.

____

22. Why did fighting begin in Massachusetts rather than one of the other colonies?

____

23. How did the Battle of Bunker Hill make the colonists more confident in declaring independence from Britain?

____

24. Why did the pamphlet *Common Sense* have such great success in the colonies?

____

25. What are some of the "unalienable rights" mentioned in the Declaration of Independence?

____

Name ______________________________ Date ________________

The following paragraph comes from the Olive Branch Petition that was sent by the colonies to the English King. Use what you have learned about reading historical documents to answer questions 26-28.

July 8, 1775

Most Gracious Sovereign:

We, your Majesty's faithful subjects . . . solemnly assure your Majesty, that we not only ardently desire [that] the former harmony between [Great Britain] and these colonies may be restored but that a concord may be established between them upon so firm a basis as to perpetuate its blessings . . .

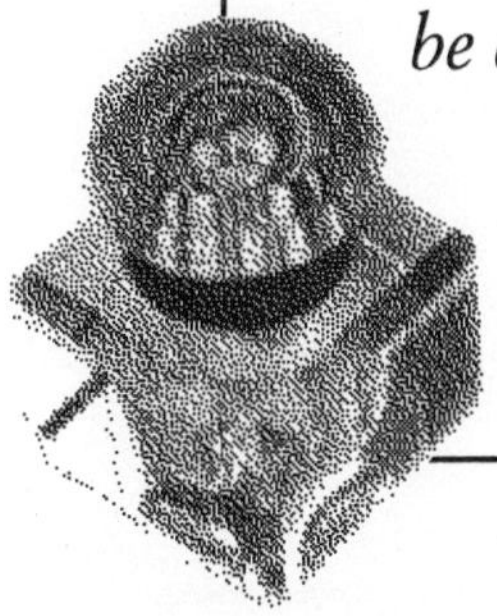

26. Was this petition written before or after the Declaration of Independence?

____

27. What does *sovereign* mean in this paragraph? ____________________

28. How do the authors of the petition describe themselves and what effect do you think they hoped for in using this description?

____

____

Name ______________________ Date ______________

Chapter 11 Test

Choose the best answer. Circle the letter next to your choice.

1. Which of the following was an important strength of the Patriot side during the War for Independence?

A. They had enough money to hire mercenaries.
B. Their generals were very experienced.
C. Their equipment was better than the British.
D. They felt enthusiasm for their cause.

2. Which of the following was an important strength of the British during the War for Independence?

A. In general, Native Americans supported the British.
B. British soldiers fought for the right to govern themselves.
C. British fighting methods worked well in America.
D. The British were helped by Swiss intervention.

3. When the war began, how did the British plan to win?

A. by waiting for the Patriots to lose faith in the war
B. by getting help from France and Spain
C. by crushing the Patriots quickly
D. by starving the Patriot forces

4. George Washington's strategy in the early part of the war was to —

A. persuade the mercenaries to join the colonies
B. fight when he had to and then retreat
C. send his troops home to build morale
D. trick the British into fighting the war in the South

5. Why did French intervention change the war?

A. The French wanted to win America for their own empire.
B. Britain could not send as many troops to fight the colonists.
C. Benjamin Franklin convinced the French to stop fighting.
D. British troops were afraid of the French.

Name ______________________ Date ______________

6. What role did Spain play during the war?

A. Spanish troops fought alongside Patriot troops.
B. Spanish troops fought alongside British troops.
C. Volunteers from Spanish territory in Louisiana attacked the British.
D. Spanish generals came to teach Patriot troops how to fight.

7. Why did the British want to move the war to the South?

A. Their troops were exhausted from the harsh northern winters.
B. The southern countryside had good places for battles.
C. They hoped to get the support of southern Loyalists.
D. They thought northern soldiers would desert the Patriot army.

8. In 1779, George Rogers Clark and his army captured forts in the —

A. Ohio Valley
B. South Carolina swamps
C. southern towns of Savannah, Charleston, and Camden
D. harbors of New York and Philadelphia

9. As a result of the Treaty of Paris in 1783, the western boundary of the United States became —

A. the Appalachian Mountains
B. the Mississippi River
C. the Rocky Mountains
D. the Pacific Ocean

10. The United States and France made separate peace treaties with Britain because —

A. France was by then the enemy of the United States.
B. The French and the British were allies.
C. The French did not trust Benjamin Franklin.
D. The Americans did not completely trust the French.

Name ______________________________ Date ________________

11. **How did the Revolution affect the lives of Native Americans?**
   A. The Native Americans who fought on the Patriot side were rewarded with rich lands.
   B. The colonists made peace treaties with the Native Americans.
   C. No matter which side they had been on, they lost their lands.
   D. Most Native Americans moved to British land in Canada.

12. **After the American Revolution, the number of free African Americans —**
   A. increased
   B. decreased
   C. stayed the same
   D. All enslaved African Americans were freed.

For questions 13-17, choose a word from the list below that matches the description. Write the word in the space provided.

intervention	**surrender**	**neutral**	**negotiate**
diplomat	**mercenary**	**revolution**	**strategy**

13. **a plan of action** ______________________

14. **a government's representative who deals with other nations**

____

15. **to give up and admit defeat** ______________________

16. **an attempt to overthrow one government and replace it with another**

____

17. **to talk over issues and try to reach an agreement**

____

Name ______________________________ Date ____________________

For questions 18–25 in the space provided. Continue your answer on the back of the sheet if you need to.

18. Where did Washington's army spend the bitter winter of 1778? ______________

19. What French nobleman fought alongside General Washington? ______________

20. Complete this chart by adding one strength and one weakness of the Patriots' army during the Revolution.

	British Army	Continental Army
Strength	wealthy country	
Weakness	fight on unfamiliar land	

21. What might have happened if Washington hadn't retreated from the British across the East River in New York?

____

22. In 1778, France entered the war on the side of the Patriots. What event was probably the key to France's entry? Explain.

____

23. What fighting method did Francis Marion use against the British?

____

24. In addition to stating the independence of the United States, what else did the Treaty of Paris do for the new nation?

____

25. What became of the Loyalists after the Revolution?

____

Name ______________________________ Date ________________

In this chapter, you have learned about making maps from written descriptions. Use the description and the partly completed map below to answer questions 26-28.

In December of 1776, Washington and his troops were on the Pennsylvania side of the Delaware River. Washington was determined to attack Trenton, on the New Jersey side. In the main part of the attack, Patriot troops would cross the river above Trenton and land near Bear Tavern. They would then march downriver to Trenton, where British troops, commanded by Colonel Rall, were located.

Washington and his men were able to complete their crossing by 3 A.M. At their landing place, Washington divided his forces into two groups. One, under John Sullivan, was to follow the River Road. The other was to follow a different road that was farther inland.

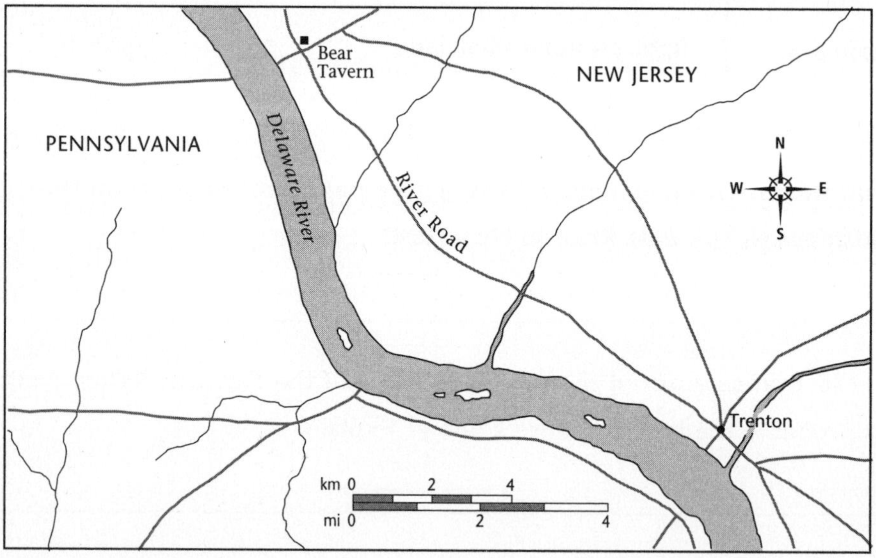

26. Mark and label the place where Washington and his troops landed after crossing the Delaware.

27. Mark the location of the British forces led by Rall.

28. Mark and label the route that the forces under John Sullivan took to Trenton once they had crossed the Delaware.

Name ______________________ Date ______________

Open-ended Response

In this unit, you learned how American colonists moved toward independence in the 1760s and 1770s. The statue at the Old North Bridge in Concord shows one of these colonists, a Minuteman.

What do you think this statue would tell us if it could come to life? Use what you have learned in this unit to write what the statue might say. Your answer can be in the form of a speech, a poem, a list of points, questions for modern Americans, or some other written form.

Use the lines below for your notes. Prepare your response on separate sheets.

Theme Project Rubric

Use this scoring rubric for a holistic assessment of each student's work on the Theme Project "Patriot or Loyalist?" on page 231 of the Student Book. You might begin by reviewing the entirety of a student's work and deciding *in general* which description most closely fits the work being evaluated. For example, you might decide that a product could *best* be described, in general, by the level 4 rubric than by the level 3.

Level 4	Level 3	Level 2	Level 1
• The project demonstrates thorough and in-depth knowledge of the views of the Patriots and Loyalists and the events leading up to the American Revolution. • The project includes one or more detailed newspaper articles and a letter. Student is a leader in role-playing activities. • Descriptions, analyses, and role-playing reflect an authentic and consistent Revolutionary Period perspective. • The work presented is clear, well-organized, and free of mechanical and grammatical errors. • The work reflects detailed research and synthesis of information and uses paraphrasing effectively.	• The project correctly describes or relates views of the Patriots and Loyalists and events leading up to the American Revolution. • The project includes at least one newspaper article and a letter. Student consistently participates in role-playing activities. • Descriptions, analyses, and role-playing mostly reflect a Revolutionary Period perspective. • The work presented is mostly clear and well-organized and has few mechanical and grammatical errors. • The work reflects research and synthesis of information and uses paraphrasing.	• The project demonstrates some misunderstandings of the views of the Patriots and Loyalists and the events leading up to the American Revolution. • The student has included only one type of work or some work that does not relate directly to the assignment. Student participates half-heartedly or inconsistently in role-playing activities. • The project needs a more consistent perspective and needs revising to better identify relationships, analyze causes, and exclude inappropriate materials. • The materials need a consistent organization scheme and have many mechanical and grammatical errors. • The materials demonstrate distinct deficiencies in research skills, including paraphrasing.	• The project shows a fundamental misunderstanding of the views of the Patriots and Loyalists and the events leading up to the American Revolution. • The materials presented fail in significant ways to meet the assignment. Student disrupts or does not contribute to role-playing activities. • The project needs to identify relationships, analyze causes, and exclude inappropriate materials. • The materials are difficult to read; no organization is apparent. • The materials provide little or no evidence of research skills, including paraphrasing.

Name ______________________ Date ______________

Performance Assessment Event

Your teacher will give you directions for using this page.

In this unit, you have learned about how American colonists in the 1760s and 1770s decided to declare independence. They had to decide whether they were Patriots or Loyalists. If they were Patriots, they may have fought in the Revolution.

Suppose the war has just ended and you are a Patriot who has been selected as an American delegate to the peace talks in Paris. On your journey to the peace talks, you must plan your opening speech to your fellow delegates at these talks.

Prepare an outline for your speech. Include an account of your personal experiences during the Revolution and your hopes for the future of your new country. Also include your ideas about the basis for the peace settlement.

Your outline will be evaluated according to the following criteria:

1. Does your outline show that you understand what happened during the Revolution?
2. Does it cover war events, hopes for the future, and what the peace settlement should be like?
3. Does it show an understanding that some events cause others to happen? Does it show an understanding of how people work together to achieve peace?
4. Does the outline state points clearly and briefly?

Possible Extensions

A. Work with a partner to develop a five minute speech that you can give at the opening of the peace talks. Divide the speech so that both partners have an equal share. Practice your speech so you can give it smoothly.

Your teacher and your classmates will evaluate your speech using the following criteria:

1. accurate and interesting details
2. style and organization of your presentation
3. reasonableness of suggested peace terms
4. equal participation of both partners

B. What if you had been a Loyalist throughout the war? Write a paragraph about what you are doing and how you are feeling at the end of the war.

Performance Assessment Tips

Performance Event

Suggest that students consider how the events of the Revolution might have affected individual Patriots. Students can brainstorm events and list them on the board. Invite students to consider how Patriots felt at the end of the war. Students can role-play a discussion of peace terms with a partner.

Review the requirements of writing an outline. Point out the importance of logical thinking in creating an outline. You might want to model the form of an outline on the board.

If your students have completed the Theme Project for Unit 4, encourage them to review the articles and letters they wrote and the role-playing they did. They should also look at their research about a real colonist.

Help students create a resource table to use in writing outlines. Possible resources include reference books, research materials, and library books. Add material from the theme projects.

For work needing revision, discuss what the problem is—missing material or lack of clarity, for example. Have the student suggest a strategy for dealing with the problem. For students who must begin over because their work has major problems, have them read some good outlines. Suggest that students start their work by listing the main headings in their outline. Once you have approved the headings, they can start to write.

Extensions

A. Suggest that pairs of students first work together to brainstorm the topics and information that their speech should cover. They might do this by creating a concept map or a list of topics. Remind them that five minutes is not a very long time for a speech, and that they should limit their topics accordingly. Once they have decided what they want to cover, they should first arrange their ideas in logical order and then divide the speech's contents between the two of them. Suggest that they do a timed practice of their speech before giving it to a larger group.

B. You might begin by holding a class brainstorming session about how a Loyalist would feel at the end of the war. Also, get students to think of the practical realities that Loyalists had to deal with: victorious Patriots were bound to resent the Loyalists' attitudes and behavior during the war.

Performance Assessment Rubric

Use this scoring rubric for a holistic assessment of each student's work on the Performance Assessment Event on page 73 of *Assessment Options*. You might begin by reviewing the entirety of a student's work and deciding *in general* which description most closely fits the work being evaluated. For example, you might decide that a product could *best* be described, in general, by the level 4 rubric rather than the level 3.

Level 4	Level 3	Level 2	Level 1
• The outline demonstrates excellent knowledge of the events of the Revolution and its outcome. • The outline covers war events, hopes for the future, and terms for a peace settlement. • The outline shows a logical ordering of points, connections between cause and effect, and an understanding of how compromise is achieved. • The outline is clear and appropriately brief. • The outline reflects excellent application of such social studies skills as using source materials, role-playing, and having historical perspective.	• The outline demonstrates good knowledge of the events of the Revolution and its outcome. • The outline covers war events, hopes for the future, and terms for a peace settlement, but there are minor omission or errors. • The outline shows a generally logical ordering of points and offers reasonable terms for compromises. • The outline is mostly clear and appropriately brief. • The student has applied some social studies skills such as using source materials, role-playing, and having historical perspective.	• The outline demonstrates some knowledge of the events of the Revolution and its outcome. There are errors or omissions in content. • Some elements that should appear in the outline are missing. • Ideas in the outline are not arranged in logical order; proposed terms are unclear or unreasonable. • The outline is often unclear. • The outline demonstrates insufficient evidence of social studies skills.	• The outline shows a lack of understanding of the Revolution and its outcome. • Several sections of the assignment are omitted. • The outline shows little or no evidence of sound thinking skills. The material presented is weakly organized or illogical. • The outline is unclear and may ramble. • The outline shows little evidence that the student used social studies skills to write it.

Name ______________________ Date ______________

Chapter 12 Test

Choose the best answer. Circle the letter next to your choice.

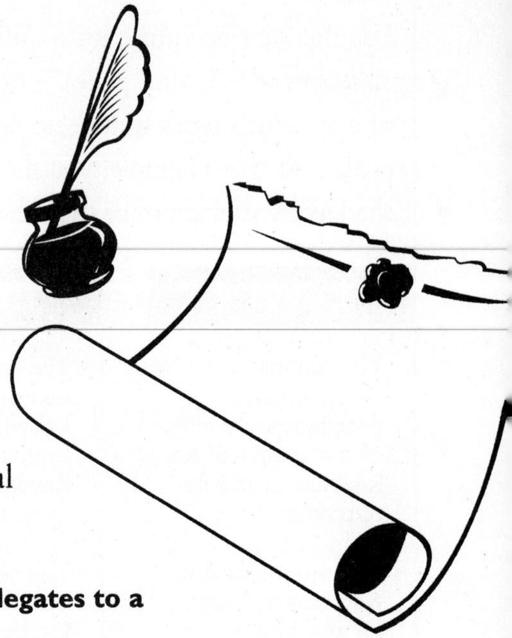

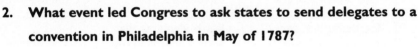

1. What was the purpose of the Northwest Ordinance of 1787?

A. It created a single, strong form of money for the country.

B. It created rules for settling new territory.

C. It set up a weak national government.

D. It let the states borrow money from the national government.

2. What event led Congress to ask states to send delegates to a convention in Philadelphia in May of 1787?

A. the passage of the Northwest Ordinance

B. a disagreement between Maryland and Virginia about the Potomac River

C. a rebellion by farmers in western Massachusetts

D. Benjamin Franklin's request for a convention

3. What was James Madison's purpose in studying the history of democratic governments?

A. He used history to help draw up plans for a republic.

B. He used history to convince the Federalists to add a Bill of Rights.

C. He hoped these examples would convince delegates to include women, African Americans, and Native Americans as citizens.

D. He was a history professor who advised convention delegates.

4. What present feature of our government is a direct result of the Great Compromise of 1787?

A. We have the Bill of Rights.

B. We can amend the Constitution.

C. In the Senate, each state has an equal number of votes; in the House of Representatives, votes are based on the state's population.

D. The President can serve only two terms.

Name ______________________________ Date ____________________

5. **The U.S. government is a federal government because —**
   A. it shares power with the states
   B. the rights of the people are protected by law
   C. it has the power to tax people
   D. each state can regulate interstate trade

6. **What has to happen for an amendment to become part of the Constitution?**
   A. A majority of voters must approve it in a national election.
   B. Three-quarters of the states must approve it.
   C. Congress, the President, and the Supreme Court must approve it.
   D. It is too late now to add an amendment to the Constitution.

7. **Members of President Washington's cabinet were responsible for —**
   A. advising the president and acting as heads of departments
   B. deciding what Washington's title should be
   C. serving in the new system of federal courts
   D. deciding which taxes were needed and collecting them

8. **Which of these actions was a goal of the Federalist party?**
   A. helping the French fight their revolution
   B. establishing a national bank
   C. helping family farms to do well
   D. ensuring that government did not grow too strong

9. **What is the MAIN advantage of the system of checks and balances?**
   A. It is efficient because each branch specializes in one kind of work.
   B. It allows more people to take part in government.
   C. It lets people handle local problems at the local level.
   D. It keeps one branch from becoming too powerful.

10. **The Constitution was ratified in 1788. Which of the following was an important reason the Constitution was ratified?**
    A. Patrick Henry spoke in favor of it.
    B. George Washington agreed to be the first President.
    C. The Northwest Ordinance was passed.
    D. The Antifederalists were promised a bill of rights.

Name ______________________________ Date ______________

For questions 11–15, choose the term from the list below that matches the description. Write the term in the space provided.

constitution	**compromise**	**amendment**	**political party**
precedent	**cabinet**	**republic**	**democracy**
executive branch	**judicial branch**	**legislative branch**	

11. a group of people with similar goals who work together to gain power in government

____

12. an agreement in which each side of an argument gives up something it wants in order to end a dispute

____

13. a written plan of how government works ______________________

14. the branch of government that makes the laws ______________________

15. a government in which people make political decisions by voting and the majority rules

____

Answer questions 16–25 in the spaces provided. Continue your answer on the back of the sheet if you need to.

16. Who is called the Father of the Constitution? ______________________

17. The first ten amendments to the United States Constitution are called the

____

18. After the Revolutionary War, why didn't the former colonies want a strong national government?

____

Name ______________________ Date ______________

19. What effect did Shays' Rebellion have on people's attitudes toward the Articles of Confederation?

____

20. Did the delegates to the constitutional convention of 1787 represent the entire population of the states? Why or why not?

____

21. How does the organization of Congress reflect the way the delegates to the Constitutional Convention compromised over the issue of representation?

____

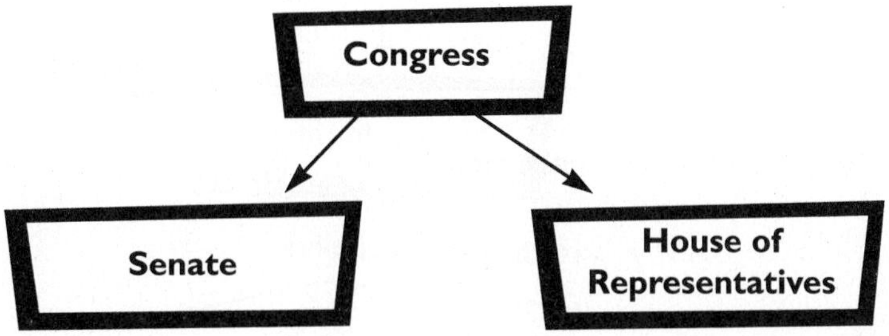

22. Give an example of a power that is shared by the federal and state governments.

____

23. Explain ONE way in which an amendment has changed the Constitution.

____

24. How did George Washington, as the first President of the United States, shape the office of the Presidency?

____

25. Contrast Hamilton's and Jefferson's views on a strong national government.

____

____

Name ______________________________ Date ____________________

The chart shows how one kind of city government works. Use your skills in working with organizational charts to answer questions 26–28.

The City Manager Type of City Government

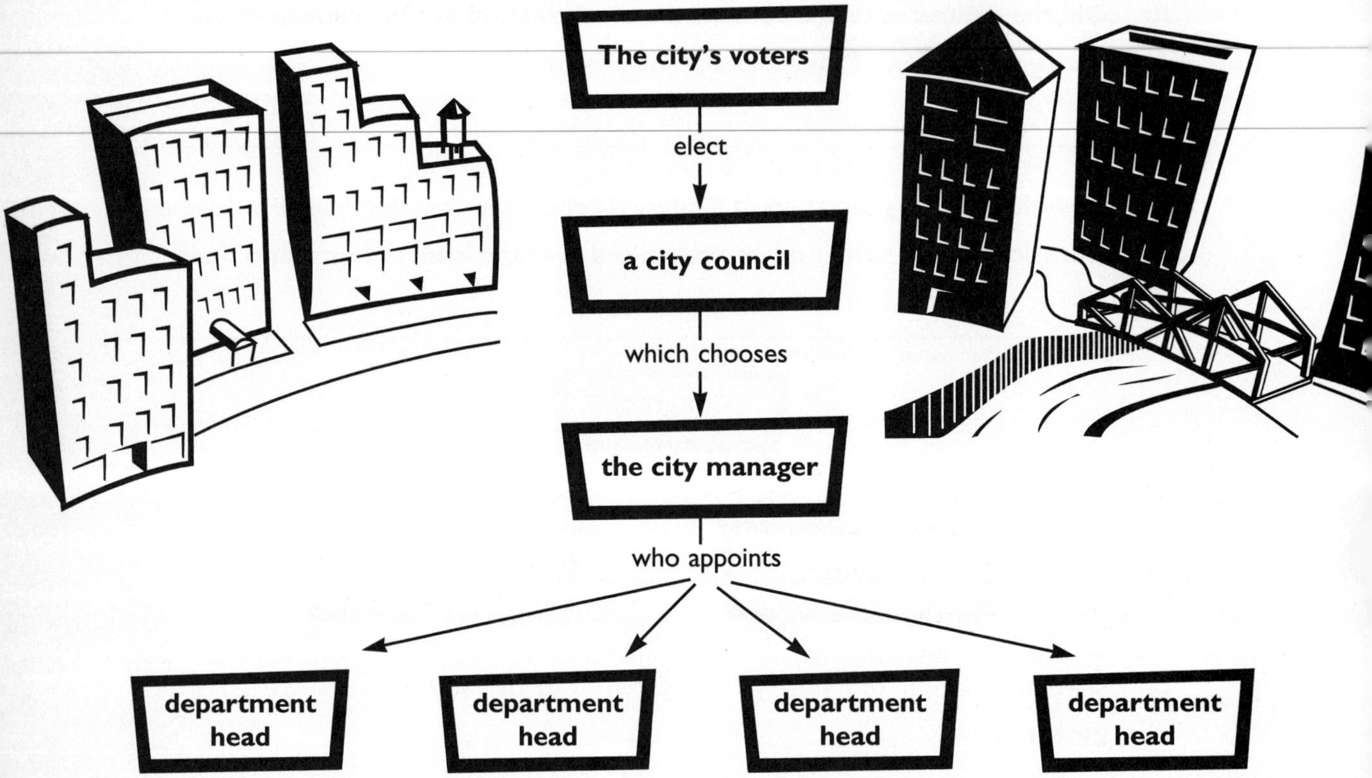

26. **In this kind of city government, how is the city manager chosen?**

____

27. **In this kind of city government, how is the city council chosen?**

____

28. **Cities have many departments, such as the police department. According to the chart, who chooses the heads of the departments in this kind of city government?**

____

Name ______________________ Date ______________

Chapter 13 Test

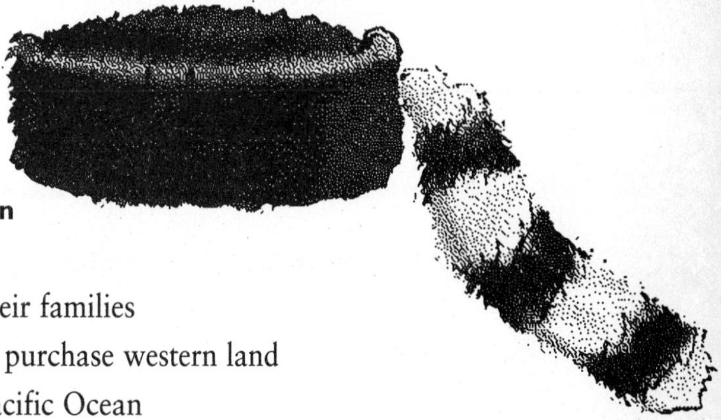

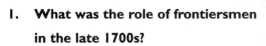

Choose the best answer. Circle the letter next to your choice.

1. What was the role of frontiersmen in the late 1700s?

A. to settle on new farms with their families
B. to pressure the government to purchase western land
C. to find a water route to the Pacific Ocean
D. to explore unsettled areas so settlers could follow

2. What problem did President Jefferson fear would result from the transfer of the Louisiana Territory from Spain to France?

A. France might try to take over the United States.
B. France might close the Mississippi River to Americans.
C. France might try to buy American land from settlers.
D. France might attack American settlers.

3. How far to the west did the Lewis and Clark expedition get?

A. St. Louis
B. the Great Plains
C. the Rocky Mountains
D. the Pacific Ocean

4. What effect did the Louis and Clark expedition have on the nation?

A. It guaranteed good relations with Native Americans.
B. It opened up a water route across the continent.
C. It helped prepare the nation for further western expansion.
D. It started a war with Spain.

5. What British activity helped draw the United States into the War of 1812?

A. Britain claimed land that Napoleon sold to the United States.
B. British merchants refused to carry American goods.
C. British sailors were flogged on British ships.
D. The British captured American sailors and forced them into the British navy.

Name ______________________________ Date ____________________

6. How was the Battle of Tippecanoe related to the War of 1812?

A. The battle happened before the war and helped lead to it.

B. The battle took place just after war was declared.

C. The battle made both sides agree to end the war.

D. The battle happened after the war and was not related to it.

7. What was the result of the British march into Washington in 1814?

A. The British burned many government buildings.

B. British forces were beaten back by American troops.

C. The President was killed by a British soldier.

D. British troops were trapped in an ambush and killed.

8. Who became a national hero during the Battle of New Orleans in 1815?

A. Dolly Madison

B. Meriwether Lewis

C. Andrew Jackson

D. Daniel Boone

9. How has the number of stars and stripes on our national flag changed since 1818?

A. The number of both stars and stripes has remained the same.

B. The number of stars and stripes has increased as the nation has grown.

C. The number of stripes has increased as the number of states has grown, but the stars have stayed the same.

D. The number of stars has increased as the number of states has grown, but the stripes have stayed the same.

10. Which of the following would an artist in the early 1800s have been MOST likely to choose as a patriotic symbol?

A. a wild turkey

B. a map of North America

C. Miss Liberty

D. a one-room schoolhouse

11. Noah Webster hoped that his dictionary would —

A. help Americans follow British rules more correctly

B. teach immigrants how to speak English

C. help create an American form of English

D. develop an interest in reading and books

Name ______________________________ Date ____________________

12. What did children study at the schoolhouse in the early 1800s?

A. the practical arts of running a farm and a household

B. reading, writing, math, and citizenship

C. spelling, reading, and biology

D. religion, foreign language, and science

For questions 13 and 14, mark and label your answers on the map below.

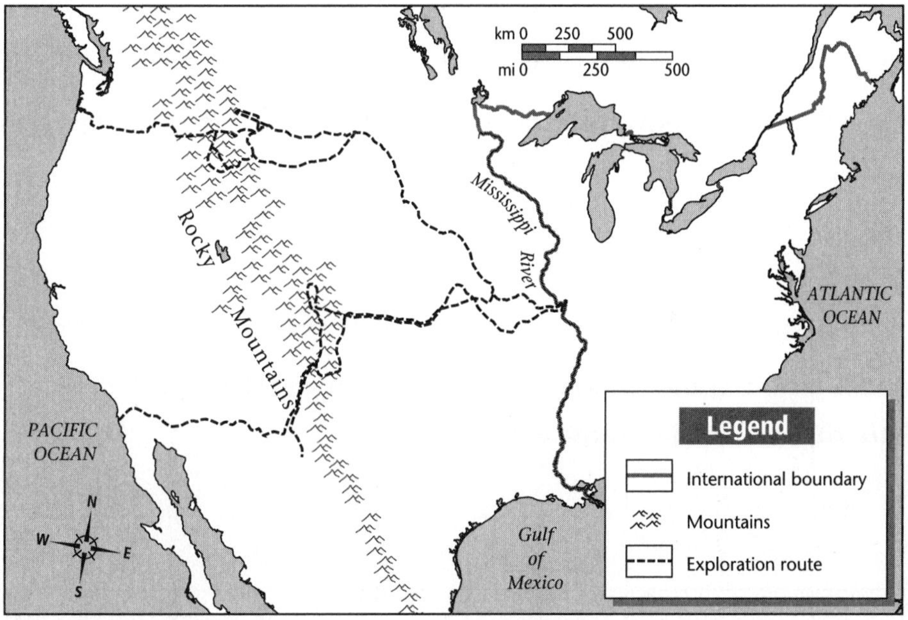

13. Shade in the area that was bought in the Louisiana Purchase.

14. Circle the beginning and end points of the Lewis and Clark expedition.

Answer questions 15–20 in the spaces provided. Continue your answer on the back of the sheet if you need to.

15. How did Daniel Boone contribute to the nation's westward expansion?

____

16. What were the TWO goals of the Lewis and Clark Expedition?

____

____

Name ______________________________ Date ________________

17. **Did Tecumseh achieve his dream? Explain why or why not.**

____

____

18. **How did the end of the War of 1812 affect American pride and unity?**

____

____

19. **Why did Parson Weems make up the story about George Washington and the cherry tree?**

____

____

20. **What is one difference between your classroom and the schoolhouse where children learned in the early 1800s?**

____

____

For questions 21–25, choose a word from the list below that matches the description. Write the word in the space provided.

expedition	**symbol**	**corps**
impressment	**frontier**	**hero**

21. **a journey undertaken by a group for a definite purpose** ________________

22. **a person who is known for a special achievement** ________________

23. **to force people into the military service** ________________

24. **a region just beyond a settled area** ________________

25. **something that stands for something else** ________________

Name ______________________________ Date ________________

Read the source material about the Lewis and Clark expedition. Then use your research skills to answer questions 26-28.

Two thousand five hundred dollars was a lot of money in 1803, but Captain Lewis had to make it go a long way in fitting out an expedition of some forty-five men for eighteen months or more. He had to think beforehand of everything that would be needed. When they were two thousand miles up the Missouri it would be too late.

He went to Lancaster, Harpers Ferry, and Philadelphia, assembling supplies, arms, ammunitions, tools, scientific instruments, medicine, and gaudy trinkets for the Indian trade, such as beads, paint, flags, bronze medals with Jefferson's head on one side and hands clasped in peace on the other.

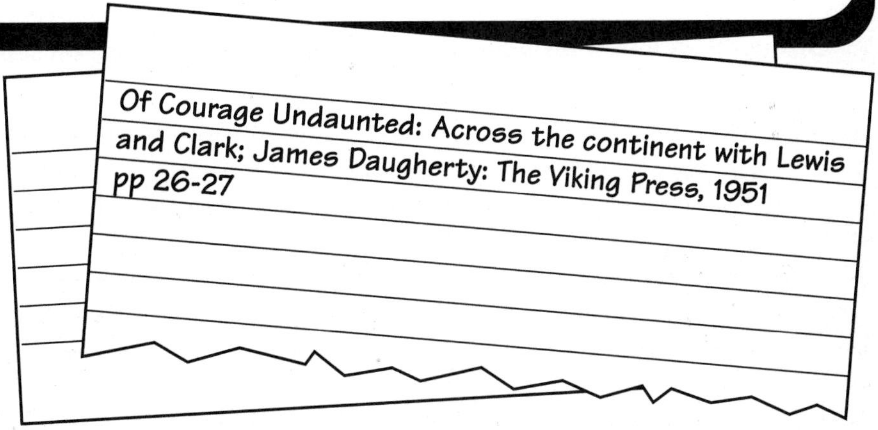

Of Courage Undaunted: Across the continent with Lewis
and Clark; James Daugherty: The Viking Press, 1951
pp 26-27

26. Who wrote the book from which this passage is taken? ________________

27. Paraphrase the first sentence of the passage.

____

____

28. Suppose you want to quote the description of the bronze medals directly. Show how you would copy the quotation.

____

____

Name ______________________________ Date ________________

Open-ended Response

In this unit, you learned about how the new nation created the Constitution and began to govern itself. George Washington favored the adoption of the Constitution. He recognized that the Constitution wasn't perfect, but he believed that people in the future could decide on any amendments that were necessary to make the Constitution work. Washington believed that under the Constitution, power would always be in the hands of the people.

What are some ways that the Constitution puts power in the hands of the people of the United States? Use what you have learned in this unit to answer that question. Draw a chart, write a paragraph, or create another way of showing the truth of Washington's belief.

Use the lines below for your notes. Prepare your response on separate sheets.

Theme Project Rubric

Use this scoring rubric for a holistic assessment of each student's work on the Theme Project, "Constitutional Expert," on page 301 of the Student Book. You might begin by reviewing the entirety of a student's work and deciding *in general* which description most closely fits the work being evaluated. For example, you might decide that a product could *best* be described, in general, by the level 4 rubric than by the level 3.

Level 4	Level 3	Level 2	Level 1
• The project demonstrates thorough and in-depth knowledge of the 1787 Convention and the provisions and effects of the Constitution. • The project includes a chart, drawings, and an editorial. Student is a leader in role-playing activities. • The project includes insightful analysis, evaluation, and stating and supporting a point of view. • Visuals and writing are clear and well-organized. • The work reflects detailed research and synthesis of information and uses visuals and paraphrasing effectively.	• The project correctly describes the 1787 Convention and the provisions and effects of the Constitution. • The project includes several types of work, such as a chart, drawings, and an editorial. Student consistently participates in role-playing activities. • The project includes some analysis and evaluation and states and supports a point of view. • Visuals and writing are mostly clear and well-organized. • The work reflects research and synthesis of information and uses visuals and paraphrasing appropriately.	• The project demonstrates some misunderstandings of the 1787 Convention and the provisions and effects of the Constitution; it may include irrelevant material. • The project includes only one or two types of work. Student participates half-heartedly or inconsistently in role-playing. • The project demonstrates distinct weaknesses in analysis or in expressing a point of view and/or supporting it with relevant evidence. • The materials need a consistent organization scheme and have many mechanical and grammatical errors. Visuals are difficult to interpret. • The materials demonstrate distinct deficiencies in research skills, including paraphrasing.	• The project shows a fundamental misunderstanding of the 1787 Convention and the provisions and effects of the Constitution. • The materials presented fail in significant ways to meet the assignment. Student disrupts or does not contribute to role-playing activities. • There is little evidence of analysis, evaluation, presenting a point of view, or gathering and offering evidence to support a position. • The materials are difficult to read; no organization is evident. Visuals are missing or features are not recognizable. • The materials provide little or no evidence of research skills, including paraphrasing.

Name ______________________________ Date ________________

Performance Assessment Event

Your teacher will give you directions for using this page.

In this unit, you have learned about how Americans created a new constitution. Using this constitution, we have been governing ourselves for over 200 years.

After the Constitution was written, it had to be ratified by the states. The Federalists supported the ratification of the Constitution. The anti-Federalists were not so sure that the Constitution should be ratified.

Think of yourself in the role of a leader in one of the states. You will be participating in a debate about ratifying the Constitution. You can choose to be either a Federalist or an anti-Federalist. Write the notes you will use to argue in the debate.

Your teacher will use the following criteria to evaluate your notes:

1. They show that you know about the Constitution and the Federalist and anti-Federalist positions.
2. They contain information that is important in backing up the points you are making.
3. They are logically organized and are designed to persuade people that your point of view is right.
4. They are clearly written.

Possible Extensions

A. Form a debating team for either the Federalist or anti-Federalist side. Work with your team to build the strongest possible arguments for your side. First, decide what your arguments will be. Then divide your major points among the members of your team. Each member should then research his or her points and write an argument in support of them. Practice your arguments as a group so you can deliver them smoothly.

Your teacher and your classmates will evaluate your debate using the following criteria:

1. accurate and convincing arguments
2. style and organization of your presentation
3. participation of all team members

B. Write a newspaper editorial that takes either the Federalist or the anti-Federalist point of view on the ratification of the Constitution. In your editorial, address the major issues that concerned people about ratification.

Performance Assessment Tips

Performance Event

Suggest that students consider why Federalists supported the Constitution and why anti-Federalists opposed it. Students can brainstorm arguments for each side and list them on the board.

If your students have completed the Theme Project for Unit 5, encourage them to review the charts they made, the editorials they wrote, and debates they had. They should also look at their research about a Supreme Court case involving the Bill of Rights.

Help students create a resource table to use in preparing notes. Possible resources include a copy of the Constitution, reference books, and books about debating. Add material from theme projects if your students have done these projects.

Review the requirements of writing notes and of making persuasive arguments. Emphasize the importance of acknowledging and answering arguments on the opposing side of the question. Also emphasize the necessity of supporting a point of view with specific facts and reasons.

Students can role-play a debate with a partner playing the part of the opposing side.

For work needing revision, have students clarify which side they are on. Suggest one argument for that side and ask the students what kinds of notes would support the argument. Have them use the same process independently for other arguments.

Students whose work has major problems may have to begin over. Suggest that they start their work with one sentence that states an argument and then make notes of information supporting the argument. Once you have approved the sentence and the notes, they can start to prepare additional notes.

Extensions

A. Group students into debating teams for either the Federalist or anti-Federalist side. Each group should include some students who have mastered the unit's concepts and others whose understanding of those concepts is weaker.

Supply students with information about how to conduct a debate. Encourage teams to build strong arguments and to practice delivering them. Draw opposing teams and have the two teams debate each other. Tell students that their individual performances will be evaluated as well as the team's performance as a whole.

B. Provide models of newspaper editorials for students to examine. Encourage proficient writers to experiment with different tones—serious, humorous, angry, friendly, and so forth.

Performance Assessment Rubric

Use this scoring rubric for a holistic assessment of each student's work on the Performance Assessment Event on page 88 of *Assessment Options*. You might begin by reviewing the entirety of a student's work and deciding *in general* which description most closely fits the work being evaluated. For example, you might decide that a product could *best* be described, in general, by the level 4 rubric rather than the level 3.

Level 4

- The notes demonstrate clear and thorough knowledge of the Constitution and of the Federalist and anti-Federalist positions.
- The notes contain relevant information for a debate.
- The notes are logically organized and designed to persuade an audience.
- The notes are clear.
- The notes reflect excellent application of such social studies skills as analyzing information, using source materials, and building persuasive arguments.

Level 3

- The notes demonstrate knowledge of the Constitution and of the Federalist and anti-Federalist position.
- The notes contain relevant information for a debate but with some omissions or irrelevant information.
- Most of the organization is logical. Overall, it is persuasive.
- The notes are generally clear.
- The student has applied some social studies skills such as analyzing information, using source materials, and building persuasive arguments.

Level 2

- The notes demonstrate limited knowledge of the Constitution. There are errors or omissions in content or confusion regarding the Federalist and anti-Federalist positions.
- Much of the information is irrelevant to the purpose.
- The notes lack logical organization. Little of the material is effective in persuading an audience.
- The notes are somewhat unclear.
- The student has applied social studies skills such as analyzing information, using source materials, and building persuasive arguments, but has some weakness in skills.

Level 1

- The notes show a lack of understanding of the Constitution and the Federalist and anti-Federalist positions.
- Several sections of the assignment are omitted.
- The notes show little or no evidence of sound thinking skills. The material presented is weakly organized or illogical.
- The notes are unclear.
- The notes do not show evidence that the student used social studies skills to write them.

Name ______________________ Date ______________

Chapter 14 Test

Choose the best answer. Circle the letter next to your choice.

1. Which of the following statements about Andrew Jackson is NOT true?

A. He was a hero in the War of 1812.

B. He increased the power of the Bank of the United States.

C. He was a "self-made man."

D. Many poor people voted for him.

2. Why did Congress pass the Indian Removal Act in 1830?

A. so settlers could have the rich land of the West

B. so canals could be built on Native American land

C. because the Supreme Court ruled that this should be done

D. so the Bank of the United States could buy land

3. What effect did Fulton's steamboat have on the nation's development?

A. Interchangeable parts were adopted in many businesses.

B. Canals were built.

C. Railroads linked major cities across the country.

D. Spinning mills were built.

4. How did many workers' jobs change in the modern manufacturing system of mass production?

A. Workers took more pride in their work.

B. Workers needed more skill to make goods.

C. Workers had to work at a machine.

D. Workers now had much more free time.

5. What effect did the invention of the cotton gin have on slavery?

A. Fewer enslaved workers were needed to produce cotton.

B. Slavery spread to the cotton factories in the North.

C. The demand for enslaved workers increased.

D. The invention had no real effect on slavery.

Name ______________________________ Date ____________________

6. Which of the following was NOT a problem of city life in the North in the 1800s?

A. There were fewer factory jobs than in the South.

B. Living conditions were crowded.

C. Disease spread in the population.

D. Many people were poor and did not have good job skills.

7. What was the purpose of the Underground Railroad?

A. to deliver abolitionist newspapers in the South

B. to inspire people to stop drinking alcohol

C. to spread the words of the Second Great Awakening

D. to help African Americans escape from slavery

8. What problem in America did Dorothea Dix work to change?

A. the lack of education for African American children

B. the crime of family violence caused by alcohol

C. the overcrowding in tenement housing

D. the treatment of the mentally ill

Election Year	Total Number of Votes
1824	356,038
1828	1,143,450

9. The table shows the number of votes cast in the elections of 1824 and 1828. Which of the following accounts for the change?

A. Women were able to vote.

B. Western states gave suffrage to all white men.

C. Free African Americans were able to vote.

D. People were paid to vote in 1828.

10. In the mid-1800s, how did the South compare to the North?

A. The South was largely agricultural and the North was industrial.

B. Both the North and South were industrial.

C. The South was largely industrial and the North was agricultural.

D. Neither the South nor the North had much industry before 1875.

Name ______________________________ Date ________________

For questions 11–15, chose the term from the list below that matches the description. Write the term in the space provided.

overseer	**interchangeable parts**	**abolitionist**
tenement	**suffrage**	**temperance**
Industrial Revolution	**candidate**	**canal**
Underground Railroad		

11. **the great changes that began in England in the middle and late 1700s with a series of inventions**

____

12. **the right to vote** ______________________________

13. **a run-down apartment building located in a city** ____________________

14. **a person running for political office** ______________________________

15. **a person who fought against slavery** ______________________________

Answer questions 16–25 in the space provided. Continue your answer on the back of the sheet if you need to.

16. **The inventor of both the cotton gin and interchangeable parts was**

____

17. **The "Declaration of Sentiments and Resolutions" issued at the Seneca Falls Convention of 1848 demanded**

____

18. **By 1822, new states like Ohio and Tennessee had a different position on suffrage than the 13 original states. Explain the difference.**

____

____

Name ______________________________ Date ______________

19. **What was the Trail of Tears?**

____

20. **How did the building of canals and railroads affect the economy of the western states? Explain why.**

____

____

21. **What advantages did mill work offer New England farm girls? What were the disadvantages?**

____

____

22. **How did enslaved workers resist their conditions?**

____

23. **In the mid-1800s, many immigrants came to the United States from Ireland and Germany. Compare why these immigrants came and where they settled.**

____

____

24. **How did the antislavery movement help lead to the women's rights movement?**

____

____

25. **A number of public schools in this country are named after Horace Mann. Why is this an appropriate honor for Mann?**

____

Name ______________________________ Date ______________

Use what you have learned about comparing line and circle graphs to answer questions 26–28.

Immigration, 1820–1860

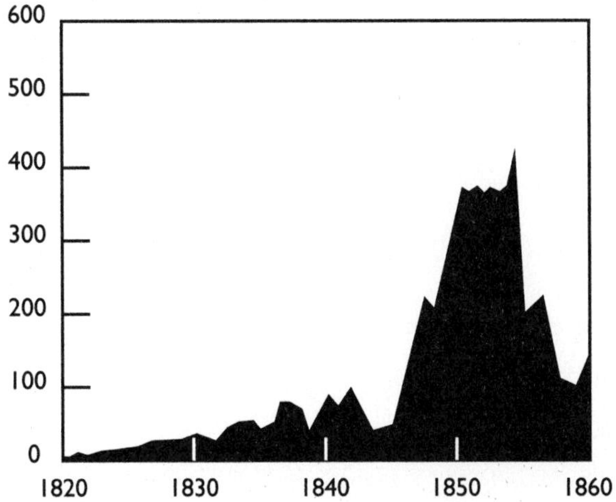

Where Immigrants Came from in 1854

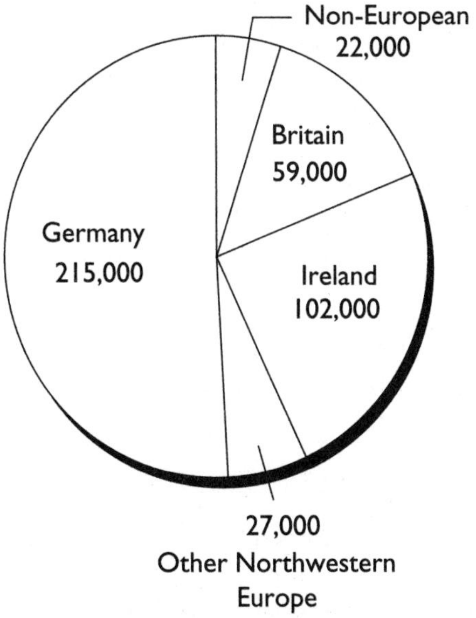

26. What does the circle graph show? What does each section show?

____

27. From the mid-1840s to the mid-1850s, what general trend does the line graph show?

____

28. One kind of graph shows change over time; the other compares amounts at one time. If you wanted to show how many girls graduated from high school in 1920, 1925, 1950, and 1975, which type of graph would you use — line or circle?

____

Name ______________________________ Date ____________________

Chapter 15 Test

Choose the best answer. Circle the letter next to your choice.

1. The MAIN reason that Anglo-Americans settled in Texas in the late 1820s was that —

A. they wanted to expand U.S. territory
B. land there was cheaper
C. they hoped to start a new nation
D. oil had been discovered

2. What was the immediate result of the Battle of San Jacinto?

A. Texas became an independent nation.
B. The United States annexed Texas.
C. Mexico outlawed slavery in Texas.
D. The defeat of Texans united them for future battles.

3. What caused the Mexican War?

A. the battle of the Alamo
B. Mexico's laws about slavery
C. the capture of Mexico's president
D. a boundary disagreement

4. As a result of the Treaty of Guadalupe Hidalgo, the U.S. —

A. gained large amounts of Mexican silver
B. experienced an increase in population as Mexicans came to live in the U.S.
C. took over the Mexican government.
D. gained land stretching from Texas to the Pacific Ocean

5. Why were thousands of Americans eager to move to Oregon in the 1840s?

A. They came to Oregon to find gold.
B. They were Mormons who hoped to escape religious persecution.
C. They had read about Oregon's mild climate and good soil.
D. They planned to raise cattle.

Name ______________________________ Date ____________________

Use the map to answer questions 6 and 7.

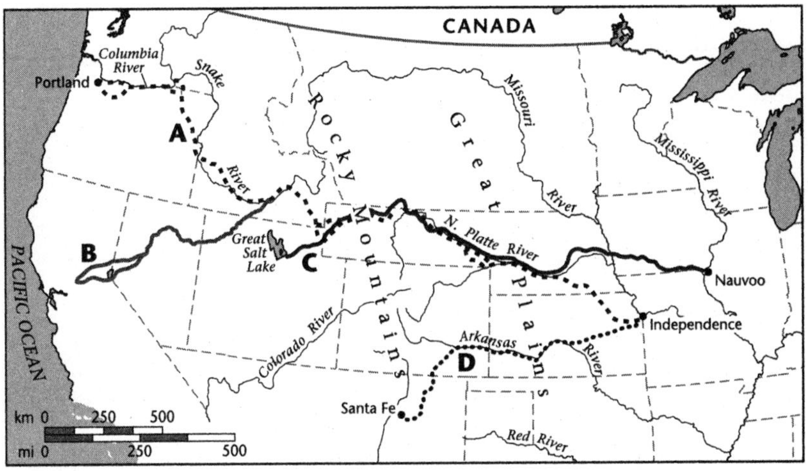

6. Which trail on the map shows the Oregon Trail?

A. Trail A

B. Trail B

C. Trail C

D. Trail D

7. Which trail did Brigham Young and his group follow?

A. Trail A

B. Trail B

C. Trail C

D. Trail D

8. Why did a group of people go west with Brigham Young?

A. to make money from gold and silver mines

B. to express their Manifest Destiny

C. to trade with Native Americans

D. to escape religious intolerance

9. The name *forty-niners* comes from the —

A. latitude where gold was first found

B. year many of the gold-seekers arrived

C. percentage of miners who actually found some gold

D. method used to separate gold from sand

Name ______________________________ Date ______________

10. California's population grew very quickly between 1848 and 1850. The people who came were —

A. from all over the world

B. Eastern families hoping for a new start

C. pioneers from Oregon

D. cowboys and soldiers from other parts of the west

11. What role did the Comstock Lode play in the settlement of Nevada?

A. Its rich farmland convinced many to come west.

B. After the Comstock Lode ran out, people left California to settle in Nevada.

C. The Comstock Lode caused a silver rush that brought people to Nevada.

D. The Comstock Lode was such a dangerous place that it gave Nevada a bad reputation.

12. The population in a boomtown tends to grow —

A. slowly and steadily

B. very quickly

C. in very unpredictable ways

D. not at all

Answer questions 13-20 in the spaces provided. Continue your answer on the back of the sheet if you need to.

13. The rallying cry of Sam Houston's army was "Remember the

____

14. Which trail opened travel to New Mexico and the Southwest?

____

15. In the 1820s Mexico encouraged Anglo-Americans to settle in Texas. How did this lead to Texas' independence?

____

____

16. How did the idea of Manifest Destiny contribute to the Mexican War?

____

Name ______________________ Date ______________

17. **What were some of the hardships faced by pioneers on the Oregon Trail?**

____

18. **How does the geography of the West help explain the importance of the main trails to pioneers?**

____

19. **James Marshall and Johann Sutter wanted to keep the discovery of gold at Sutter's mill a secret. Sam Brannan, who owned a general store, wanted people to know about it. Explain why Marshall and Sutter's feelings differed from Brannan's.**

____

____

20. **What led to the founding of towns like Tombstone, Deadwood, and Cripple Creek? What happened to many of these towns in the end?**

____

For questions 21–25, choose the term from the list below that matches the definition. Write the term in the space provided.

boomtowns	**dispute**	**annexation**	**Continental Divide**
Manifest Destiny	**pass**	**forty-niners**	

21. **an opening through a chain of mountains** ______________

22. **the high crest of the Rocky Mountains, from which rivers flow toward the east and the west**

____

23. **the belief that it was the future of the United States to expand across the continent**

____

24. **the joining of a territory to a nation** ______________

25. **to argue** ______________

Name ______________________________ Date ________________

Use what you have learned about reading contour maps to answer questions 26–28. The map shows part of Yosemite National Park in the mountains of California. The contour interval on the map is 200 feet.

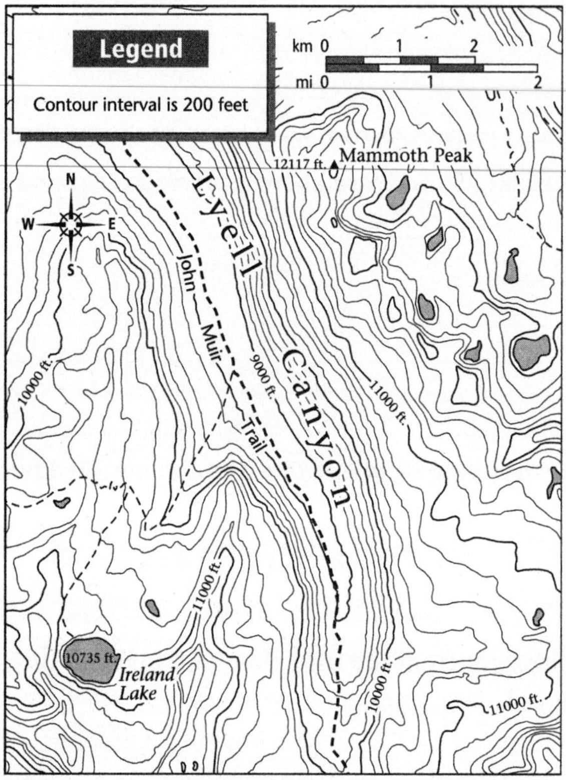

26. What is the elevation of Mammoth Peak? ______________________

27. Why do you suppose the John Muir Trail was laid out where it was?

____

28. How can you tell that the canyon is steeper on the east side than on the west side?

____

Name ______________________ Date ______________

Open-ended Response

In this unit, you learned how Americans in the first half of the 1800s explored new frontiers. Many Americans pushed westward into new regions.

In the 1840s, settlers headed west to Oregon. Suppose you were a member of a family headed west along the Oregon trail. Many things might happen along the way, and you would have many different feelings about what you do, see, and hear. Think of a way to show what you would experience and how you might feel about it. You can make a list, or write a diary entry, or draw a picture with labels that explain what is happening.

Use the lines below for your notes. Prepare your response on separate sheets.

Theme Project Rubric

Use this scoring rubric for a holistic assessment of each student's work on the Theme Project, "Journey Across America," on page 363 of the Student Book. You might begin by reviewing the entirety of a student's work and deciding *in general* which description most closely fits the work being evaluated. For example, you might decide that a product could *best* be described, in general, by the level 4 rubric than by the level 3.

Level 4	Level 3	Level 2	Level 1
• The trip record demonstrates thorough and in-depth knowledge of U.S. geography and of how people moved westward in the 1830s. • The trip record includes many of the following: a route map, calculations, drawings, and letters. • The trip record shows a creative extension of learned material, analyzing routes, evaluating transportation, and describing an historically plausible journey. • Maps are clear and easily readable; writing is clear and well-organized. • The trip record reflects detailed research and synthesis of information and uses map features, visuals, and paraphrasing effectively.	• The trip record demonstrates knowledge of U.S. geography and of how people moved westward in the 1830s. • The trip record includes several pieces of work, such as maps, calculations, drawings, and letters. • The trip record shows some evidence of using analysis and evaluation to create an historically plausible journey. • Maps, visuals, and writing are mostly clear and well-organized. • The trip record reflects research and synthesis of information and uses map features, visuals, and paraphrasing appropriately.	• The trip record demonstrates misunderstandings of U.S. geography and of how people moved westward in the 1830s. • The trip record includes only one or two types of work or some work that does not relate directly to the frontier movement. • The trip is not historically plausible; the trip record demonstrates limited skills in analysis and evaluation. • The trip record is difficult to read and poorly organized. Titles and labels are missing or unclear. • The trip record demonstrates distinct deficiencies in map skills and in research skills, including paraphrasing.	• The trip record shows a fundamental misunderstanding of U.S. geography and of how people moved westward in the 1830s. • The trip record fails in significant ways to meet the assignment. • There is little evidence of skills in analysis or evaluation. The trip is either illogical or historically impossible. • The trip record is difficult to read; no organization is evident. Map is missing or features are not recognizable. • The trip record provides little or no evidence of map making or research skills.

Name ______________________ Date ______________

Performance Assessment Event

Your teacher will give you directions for using this page.

In this unit, you have learned about how Americans explored new frontiers in the first half of the 1800s. Americans pushed westward, carried out an industrial revolution, and launched reform movements, all ways of crossing frontiers.

Suppose you are a movie director, planning to make a movie called *Frontier!* To sell your movie idea to a studio, you need to prepare a simple storyboard showing what happens in the movie. A storyboard is a series of sketches that show the major events and characters in a story, movie, or play. The events are arranged in the order in which they happen.

To evaluate your storyboard, your teacher will look for the following points:

1. Does it show a knowledge of the United States in the first half of the 19th century — and a knowledge of frontiers?
2. Does it show events that are right for a frontier movie?
3. Does it show history as part of a fictional story?
4. Are the scenes easy to understand?

Possible Extensions

A. With a team of classmates, select one storyboard and create a script for a specific scene on that storyboard. Rehearse the scene and present it to your class.

The scene will be evaluated according to the following criteria:

1. interest level and historical accuracy
2. style and organization of the dialogue
3. participation of all team members

B. Create an advertising campaign for the movie. Design newspaper ads or posters that will make people want to see the movie.

Performance Assessment Tips

Performance Event

If your students have completed the Theme Project for Unit 6, encourage them to review the maps they made, the routes they planned, and the pictures they drew. They should also look at their research on the letters and diaries of people who went west. The theme projects might form part of a resource table that students use in creating their storyboards. Additional resources might include frontier stories, reference books, and books of artwork and photographs.

Suggest that students consider the challenges posed by the frontier. Students can brainstorm challenges and list them on the board. The discussion can be broadened to include many types of frontiers. Point out that any story, whether it is a book, movie, or play, usually involves conflict of some sort. The class might brainstorm possible types of conflicts involving frontiers.

Review the requirements of preparing a storyboard. Point out the importance of having a clear beginning, middle, and end. Remind students that movies often feature dramatic events. Also, the storyboards should

Students may benefit from discussing the structures of movies and television programs they have seen. You may want to analyze the dramatic structure of a movie or program that is familiar to students.

Students can work with a partner be sure their storyboards show clear beginnings, middles, and ends.

For work needing revision, point out where the storyboard has strengths and where it has weaknesses. Invite students to suggest ways of improving weak areas.

For students who must begin over, have them look at some good storyboards. Suggest that they start their work by creating a verbal story map that shows the main events in the movie. Once you have approved the story map, they can start to prepare the storyboard.

Extensions

A. Show students how to use speaker tags in writing dialogue. Also tell them what stage directions are and have them think of appropriate stage directions for their scenes. Students can then rehearse the scene and present it to the class. You may want to videotape the scene.

B. Have students bring a selection of movie advertisements to class. They should look at the ads to see what techniques are used for sparking viewers' interest. They can then try to use some of these techniques for their ads or posters. Provide art supplies—paper, markers, and so forth—as necessary.

Performance Assessment Rubric

Use this scoring rubric for a holistic assessment of each student's work on the Performance Assessment Event on page 103 of *Assessment Options*. You might begin by reviewing the entirety of a student's work and deciding *in general* which description most closely fits the work being evaluated. For example, you might decide that a product could *best* be described, in general, by the level 4 rubric rather than the level 3.

Level 4

- The storyboard demonstrates excellent knowledge of the United States in the first half of the 19th century and of the concept of frontiers.
- The storyboard contains a series of events appropriate for a frontier movie.
- The storyboard shows a creative extension of history to a fictional story. Events are logically ordered and historically appropriate.
- The material is clearly illustrated.
- The storyboard reflects excellent application of such social studies skills as sequencing, using source materials, creating visual materials, and having historical perspective.

Level 3

- The storyboard demonstrates knowledge of the United States in the first half of the 19th century and of the concept of frontiers.
- The storyboard contains a series of events that are mostly appropriate for a frontier movie.
- The storyboard shows some creative thinking. In general, events are logically ordered and historically appropriate.
- The material is generally clear.
- The student has applied social studies skills such as sequencing, using source materials, creating visual materials, and having historical perspective.

Level 2

- The storyboard demonstrates some knowledge of the frontier, but there are errors or omissions in content.
- Key story events are missing or unclear.
- Events are not all in logical order and some may be historically incorrect. Little creative thinking is shown.
- The storyboard is somewhat difficult to follow.
- The student has applied social studies skills such as sequencing, using source materials, creating visual materials, and having historical perspective, but has some weakness in skills.

Level 1

- The storyboard shows little understanding of the frontier.
- The storyboard does not contain a clear sequence of events.
- The storyboard shows little or no evidence of creative thinking. The material presented is illogical and historically incorrect.
- The storyboard is put together in such a way that it is very difficult to follow.
- The storyboard shows little evidence that the student used social studies skills to prepare it.

Name ______________________________ Date ________________

Chapter 16 Test

Choose the best answer. Circle the letter next to your choice.

1. The Compromises of 1820 and 1850 tried to resolve the North's and the South's different points of view about —

A. the spread of slavery to new states
B. ending slavery everywhere in the Union
C. economic growth
D. the system of representation in Congress

2. Why did Abraham Lincoln's election cause South Carolina to secede from the Union?

A. Lincoln was known to be against slavery.
B. Troops fired on Fort Sumter.
C. The Supreme Court decided that Dred Scott was not free.
D. Lincoln defeated a candidate from South Carolina.

3. One strength the Confederates had in the beginning of the Civil War was —

A. more railroads than the North
B. more people than the North
C. some of the best generals to lead their army
D. more money than the North

4. The surrender of Vicksburg was particularly important because it —

A. allowed the South new hope for victory
B. gave the North control of the Mississippi River
C. proved how technology had changed warfare
D. kept Britain from entering the war on the Southern side

5. Why did Lincoln proclaim the emancipation of slaves just after the battle of Antietam?

A. Virginia seceded after the battle.
B. The Confederacy elected Jefferson Davis as its president.
C. The Union won the battle.
D. The Union lost the battle.

Name ______________________________ Date ________________

6. **The Massachusetts 54th's attack on Fort Wagner proved —**
   A. the importance of control of the Mississippi River
   B. the importance of control of routes to the West
   C. the dedication of African American troops
   D. Lincoln's good judgment in choosing Grant as general

7. **Before the Civil War, most nurses were —**
   A. from the North
   B. from the South
   C. enslaved
   D. men

8. **During the Civil War, life was especially difficult for people living on farms in the upper South because —**
   A. only farmers were drafted to serve in the Confederate army
   B. farmers paid higher taxes than people in cities
   C. the Confederate army often took animals and crops
   D. farmers were punished for the Richmond riots

Use the timeline to answer questions 9 and 10.

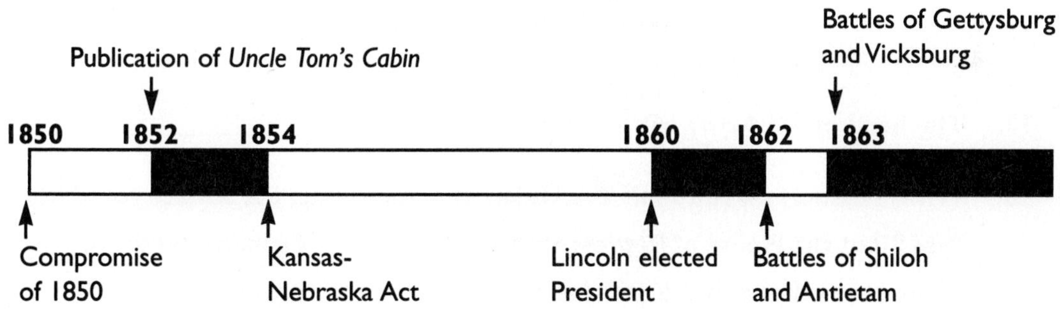

9. **What event occurred before the Kansas-Nebraska Act?**
   A. siege of Vicksburg
   B. raid on Harpers Ferry
   C. Lincoln's election
   D. Compromise of 1850

10. **The battle of Shiloh was fought —**
    A. in 1860
    B. the same year as the battle of Vicksburg
    C. the same year as the battle of Antietam
    D. after the battle of Gettysburg

Name ______________________________ Date ____________________

For questions 11–15, choose the term from the list below that matches the description. Write the term in the space provided.

inflation	**draft**	**volunteer**
mobilize	**contraband**	**blockade**
siege	**home front**	**secede**

11. **property taken from the enemy** ____________________

12. **to prepare for war** ____________________

13. **a drop in the value of money and a rise in prices** ____________________

14. **a system of choosing people and forcing them to join the army** ____________________

15. **for a state to leave the Union** ____________________

Answer questions 16–25 in the spaces provided. Continue your answer on the back of the sheet if you need to.

16. **Harriet Beecher Stowe wrote a book about slavery. Its title was** ____________________

____

17. **The head of the Army of Virginia was** ____________________

18. **When Missouri asked to join the Union as a slave state, the Senate voted "yes," but the House of Representatives voted "no." Explain how those votes were related to the makeup of the Senate and House of Representatives.**

____

____

19. **Explain the Dred Scott decision and how northerners felt about it.**

____

____

Name ______________________ Date ______________

20. What were some advantages the North had at the beginning of the war?

___

21. What was the purpose of the Northern naval blockade of Southern ports?

___

22. At first, President Lincoln was reluctant to end slavery. What were two reasons he changed his mind?

___

23. Describe the injustice that African American soldiers experienced in the Union army, and explain what was done about it.

___

___

24. Besides nursing, what were some of the jobs that women in the North and in the South took on during the Civil War?

___

25. How were rich men in the North and South able to avoid being soldiers? Explain why you think this was or was not fair.

___

Name ______________________________ Date ____________________

In this chapter, you have learned about comparing historical images. The picture below shows a sketch of a Union cavalryman based on a drawing by the artist Winslow Homer. Use the sketch to answer questions 26–28.

26. What details show that this person is a soldier?

____

27. How do you think this soldier is feeling?

____

28. How would a Civil War photograph of a Union cavalryman probably look different?

____

Name ______________________ Date ______________

Chapter 17 Test

Choose the best answer. Circle the letter next to your choice.

1. What was the MAIN reason that Grant succeeded in destroying the Confederacy?

A. The North felt renewed hope when Lincoln was re-elected.

B. The South could not continue without food, weapons, and railroads.

C. Confederate troops were not as well trained as Grant's soldiers.

D. Union troops were fighting on familiar home territory.

Use the map to help you answer question 2.

2. The arrows show Sherman's march through Georgia. Sherman had his troops —

A. approach slowly and with great caution

B. wait until they met the enemy face to face to attack

C. humiliate Confederate generals so soldiers would desert

D. destroy Southern agriculture, transportation, and morale

Name ______________________________ Date ____________________

3. In the summer and fall of 1864, Grant led a drive to take the city of —

A. Richmond
B. Savannah
C. Atlanta
D. Augusta

4. Toward the end of the war, Union troops —

A. outnumbered Confederate troops two to one
B. had a bigger problem with disease than Confederate troops did
C. had few good leaders
D. were still being paid but the Confederates were not

5. One of the main accomplishments of the Freedmen's Bureau was to help newly freed African Americans —

A. move to the Northern cities
B. build their own churches
C. become sharecroppers
D. learn to read and write

6. After the war, many African Americans who had once been enslaved —

A. kept working for their former owners without pay
B. sent food and clothing north to help people in need
C. took over their former owner's plantation and ran it themselves
D. chose their own names, built churches, and eagerly looked for work

7. Why was it particularly important for newly freed people in the South to have jobs?

A. They could be forced to work on a plantation without proof of a job.
B. Children could go to school only if their parents had jobs.
C. The Freedmen's Bureau would help only those who had jobs.
D. They needed cash to travel North or West in search of a better life.

Name ______________________________ Date ________________

8. **What problem did both African American and white sharecroppers face?**
   A. The land had been ruined by the effects of the Civil War.
   B. The amount of land they rented was too small to make a living on.
   C. Landlords often took advantage of them.
   D. Local stores would not give them credit.

9. **The Reconstruction plan of the Radical Republicans was specifically designed to —**
   A. allow the Southern states to pass Black Codes
   B. make the United States one country again
   C. let former Confederate leaders gain power
   D. protect the rights of African Americans

10. **Congress passed the Reconstruction Act of 1867 after most of the Southern states —**
    A. refused to ratify the 14th Amendment
    B. voted for Andrew Johnson for President
    C. elected African Americans to political office
    D. called for the impeachment of President Johnson

11. **What was the MAJOR effect of the presence of the U.S. Army in the South from 1865 to 1877?**
    A. The Army provided training for both African Americans and whites.
    B. African Americans voted and won elections.
    C. Segregation laws were enforced.
    D. Farmers made a lot of money by selling food to the Army.

12. **How did the South change after the Army left in 1877?**
    A. African Americans remained in power.
    B. Wages in Southern factories rose to equal those in the North.
    C. Southern whites regained complete power.
    D. Farmers stopped sharecropping and started growing a variety of crops.

Name ______________________________ Date ________________

For questions 13–17, choose a word from the list below that matches the description. Write the word in the space provided.

credit	**assassinate**	**redistribute**	**impeach**
Reconstruction	**segregation**	**sharecropping**	**carpetbagger**
scalawag	**desertion**		

13. **to accuse a president of being unfit to hold office** ____________________

14. **keeping different races apart** ____________________

15. **A system of payment that allows the buyer to buy something with borrowed money**

____

16. **when a soldier runs away from the army** ____________________

17. **to murder a president or other political figure** ____________________

Answer questions 18–25 in the spaces provided. Continue your answer on the back of the sheet if you need to.

18. **In what famous speech did President Lincoln remind the nation of the importance of "government of the people, by the people, and for the people"?**

____

19. **Where did Lee surrender?** ____________________

20. **How did Grant's strategy for winning the war affect Southern civilians?**

____

21. **Why did Grant feel it was important to treat the Southern troops with respect when Lee surrendered?**

____

Name ______________________________ Date ________________

22. Why do you think that newly freed African Americans were so eager to read and write?

____

23. Explain why many former slaves felt that their lives hadn't changed much after the Civil War.

____

24. Explain the two sides in the political war over Reconstruction.

____

____

25. How do did the poll tax effect African Americans?

____

In this chapter you have learned about using a CD-ROM encyclopedia. Use what you have learned to answer questions 26–28.

26. Suppose you wanted to use a CD-ROM encyclopedia to do research about Lincoln's Gettysburg Address. What would be a good key word or phrase to use?

____

27. Suppose you find the information you are looking for. What should you do if you need a copy of the information to refer to later?

____

28. Write a question related to the information in this chapter that you could research by using a CD-ROM encyclopedia.

____

____

Name ______________________________ Date ________________

Open-ended Response

In the nineteenth century, the North and the South differed in many ways. Before the Civil War, the two regions had differences in such things as their economies, their social systems, their population, and their ways of life. During the war period, the regions differed in troops and resources, and in the home front. Reconstruction brought still more differences.

How could you use a visual organizer to show some of these differences? Shown below are two types of organizers.

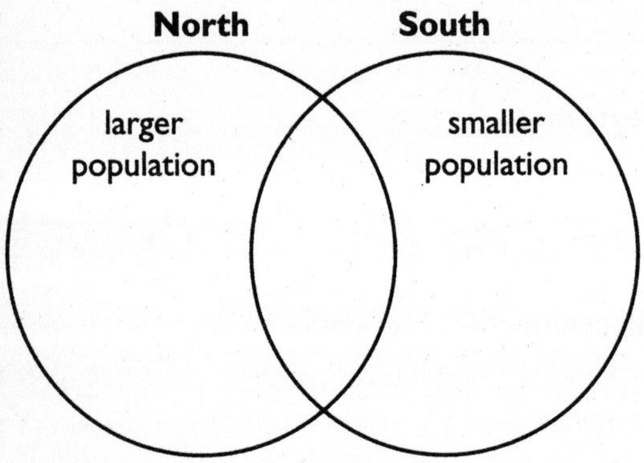

	North	South
Population	Larger	Smaller

Choose one type of organizer and use it to show some of these differences. Be sure to give your organizer a title that tells what time period is covered.

Use the lines below for your notes. Prepare your response on separate sheets.

____

____

____

____

____

____

____

Theme Project Rubric

Use this scoring rubric for a holistic assessment of each student's work on the Theme Project, "Making History," on page 423 of the Student Book. You might begin by reviewing the entirety of a student's work and deciding *in general* which description most closely fits the work being evaluated. For example, you might decide that a product could *best* be described, in general, by the level 4 rubric than by the level 3.

Level 4	Level 3	Level 2	Level 1
• The project demonstrates thorough and in-depth knowledge of life in one region of the U.S. before and after the Civil War. • The project includes many of the following: a chart, a personal account, and a tape recording. • The project analyzes events and cause-and-effect relationships, evaluates effects, and creatively extends historical ideas. • Chart is clear and easily readable, writings and tape recording are clear and well-organized. • The work reflects detailed research and synthesis of information and uses visuals effectively.	• The project demonstrates knowledge of life in one region of the U.S. before and after the Civil War. • The project includes several pieces of work, such as a chart, a personal account, and a tape recording. • The project shows some evidence of analyzing events and causal relationships and of evaluating effects. • The chart, writings, and tape recording are mostly clear and well-organized. • The work reflects research and synthesis of information and uses visuals appropriately.	• The project demonstrates misunderstandings of life before or after the Civil War. • The project includes only one or two types of work or some work that does not relate directly to the assignment. It may lack focus. on a single region. • The project demonstrates limited skills in analyzing cause and effect relationships. • Materials are difficult to read or understand and poorly organized. • The materials demonstrate distinct deficiencies in visual and/or research skills.	• The project shows a fundamental misunderstanding of life before and after the Civil War and/or of the regions of the U.S. • The work presented fails in significant ways to meet the assignment. • There is little evidence of skills in analysis or evaluation. Student may need individual instruction in cause-effect relationships. • Materials are difficult to read; no organization is evident. Chart is missing or features are not readable. • The materials provide little or no evidence of visual or research skills.

Name ______________________ Date ______________

Performance Assessment Event

Your teacher will give you directions for using this page.

Abraham Lincoln said that "human nature will not change." He meant that people will always basically be the same — there will be some weak people, some strong people, some silly people, and some wise people. However, Lincoln also believed that people could study what had happened in the past — actions that had good results and actions that made bad things happen. By thinking about these actions, people could prevent terrible events like the Civil War.

In this unit, you have learned about conflict and resolution before, during, and after the Civil War. Choose one event that you studied—either one in which people acted wisely, or one in which people acted unwisely. Create a cause-and-effect diagram about that event. The "cause" part of the diagram should describe what people did. The "effect" part should explain what happened as a result of people's actions. Finally, write a few sentences telling what people can learn from the event that will help resolve conflicts or prevent problems in the future.

Your teacher will check for these things in evaluating your work:

1. Does your work show an understanding of the Civil War?
2. Have you chosen an event in which people acted either wisely or foolishly? Have you shown what happened as a result?
3. Do you explain how people can use what they have learned from the event to help resolve conflicts?
4. Are your diagram and sentences clear and easy to understand?

Possible Extensions

A. Draw pictures illustrating the events in your cause-and-effect diagram. Contribute your diagram and pictures to a class book on the Civil War.

Your teacher will use the following criteria to evaluate your pictures:

1. whether the events are shown clearly
2. whether the pictures show both causes and effects
3. how well the pictures relate to the cause-and-effect diagram

B. Think of Lincoln's words, "Human nature will not change." Decide whether you agree or disagree. Find a partner who shares your point of view and prepare for a debate. Stage a debate with another team taking the opposite side.

Performance Assessment Tips

Performance Event

The whole class can discuss incidents related to the Civil War that show good and bad behavior. Students can brainstorm a list of incidents and put the list on the board. Also, discuss what behaviors students characterize as good/bad, silly/wise, weak/strong, and why they think so.

Review cause-effect relationships and how to diagram them. Refer to the Skills Workshop in Chapter 7, pages 180–181. Remind students that an event can have multiple effects.

If your students have completed the Theme Project for Unit 7, they might use their work as sources of ideas. Encourage them to review the event maps they made and the accounts they wrote. They should also look at their research about a real person's life.

Help students to create a resource table that they can use in describing incidents. Possible resources include research accounts, reference books, and books of artwork and photographs.

For work needing revision, provide clear directions. Help students identify and understand any errors in logical thinking, particularly in interpreting cause-effect relationships. If students' work is totally unacceptable, in their second attempt have them focus on one relatively simple event that illustrates a clear cause-effect relationship. Have them suggest one thing that can be learned from the event.

Extensions

A. You might pair good artists with students whose artistic abilities are weak. The pairs can work together to decide exactly what the pictures should show. Then the better artist can draw the parts requiring more skill, while the weaker artist can fill in the background, write captions, and so forth. Display the class book in the library.

B. Help students organize the debate. Supply them with information on how to conduct a debate. Remind them that effective debaters acknowledge their opponents' strongest arguments and then think of arguments to counter them.

Performance Assessment Rubric

Use this scoring rubric for a holistic assessment of each student's work on the Performance Assessment Event on page 118 of *Assessment Options*. You might begin by reviewing the entirety of a student's work and deciding *in general* which description most closely fits the work being evaluated. For example, you might decide that a product could *best* be described, in general, by the level 4 rubric rather than the level 3.

Level 4	Level 3	Level 2	Level 1
• The diagram and sentences demonstrate excellent knowledge of specific incidents before, during, or after the Civil War. • The chosen event shows positive or negative behavior, and the causal relationship between that event and subsequent events is clearly shown in detail. • The sentences show an insightful, valid analysis of what lessons can be learned from the incident. • The cause-effect diagram is clear and succinct. The sentences are clearly written and easy to follow. • The work reflects excellent application of such social studies skills as using source materials, interpreting historical documents, and having historical perspective.	• The diagram and sentences demonstrate good knowledge of specific incidents before, during, or after the Civil War. • The chosen event shows positive or negative behavior, and the causal relationship between that event and subsequent events is shown. • The sentences show some analysis of what lessons can be learned from the incident. • The cause-effect diagram is clear. The sentences can be understood. • The work reflects application of such social studies skills as using source materials, interpreting historical documents, and having historical perspective.	• The diagram and sentences demonstrate some knowledge of specific incidents before, during, or after the Civil War. • The chosen event shows positive or negative behavior, but the causal relationship between that event and subsequent events is not clearly shown. • The sentences show some analysis of what lessons can be learned from the incident, but the analysis may not be entirely valid or clear. • The cause-effect diagram has some valid aspects but is difficult to follow. • The work reflects weak application of such social studies skills as using source materials, interpreting historical documents, and having historical perspective.	• The diagram and sentences demonstrate little knowledge of specific incidents before, during, or after the Civil War. • The chosen event is inappropriate for showing positive or negative behavior or a cause-effect relationship. • The analysis of what can be learned from the incident is inadequate or invalid. • The cause-effect diagram is unclear. • The essay reflects little or no application of such social studies skills as using source materials, interpreting historical documents, and having historical perspective.

Name ______________________________ Date ____________________

Chapter 18 Test

Choose the best answer. Circle the letter next to your choice.

1. **One effect of the transcontinental telegraph was to decrease the need for —**
   A. railroads
   B. newspapers
   C. the pony express
   D. Morse code

2. **About how long did it take to send a telegraph message from the east coast to the west coast in the 1860s?**
   A. a few minutes
   B. about a day
   C. about 10 days
   D. almost a month

3. **Who laid most of the track in the transcontinental railroad?**
   A. formerly enslaved people who were freed after the Civil War
   B. prisoners from jails in the East and Midwest
   C. farmers and ranchers who wanted the railroad
   D. Irish and Chinese immigrants

4. **What was one way the transcontinental railway tied the country together?**
   A. Raw materials from the East went to factories in the West.
   B. Products from the West could be shipped to markets in the East.
   C. Trade between the North and South helped heal the wounds of the Civil War.
   D. Gold miners could reach California.

5. **Why did ranchers drive cattle north from Texas to places like Abilene?**
   A. Cattle were easier to raise further north.
   B. The government was offering free grazing land in the north.
   C. So cattle could be shipped to eastern buyers.
   D. Ranchers could not compete with Texas farmers for land.

Name ______________________________ Date ____________________

6. One of cowboys' MAIN problems during cattle drives was —

A. stampedes

B. attacks by rival groups of cowboys

C. storms

D. cattle joining buffalo herds

7. How did many of the Plains Indians react to the government's reservation policy?

A. They became cattle ranchers.

B. They moved west to California.

C. They went to work in Eastern cities.

D. They fought for their homelands.

8. According to Wovoka's vision, doing the Dance of the Ghosts would —

A. unite all Native Americans to overthrow the government

B. bring death to white soldiers and settlers

C. bring dead Native American warriors to life

D. help his people forget their former culture

9. What was the purpose of the Homestead Act?

A. to encourage people to move to cities

B. to provide free lumber to build houses

C. to drive out Native Americans

D. to encourage people to settle and farm the land

10. Settlers found farming on the Great Plains so difficult because —

A. many different groups of people lived close together

B. forests had to be cleared before the land could be farmed

C. there was often not enough rain to grow crops

D. herds of buffalo used the land for grazing

11. The MAIN reason that farmers joined the Grange was to —

A. band together to buy supplies and equipment more cheaply

B. work on each other's farms at harvest time

C. support research on new ways to grow crops

D. relieve the loneliness of life on the plains

Name ______________________ Date ______________

12. William Jennings Bryan helped farmers gain —

A. higher prices for their wheat
B. a stronger voice in national politics
C. new irrigation projects sponsored by the government
D. new lands opened to settlement

For questions 13-17, choose the term from the list below that matches the description. Write the term in the space provided.

telegraph	**dry farming**	**sodbuster**	**pony express**
homestead	**Grange**	**reservation**	**cattle trail**

13. land claimed by a settler ______________________

14. land set aside for Native Americans ______________________

15. a device that uses electrical energy to send signals over wires

____

16. a mail service that kept people across the United States in touch with each other

____

17. a technique in which farmers left a field unplanted for a season so the field could store moisture

____

Answer questions 18-25 in the spaces provided. Continue your answer on the back of the sheet if you need to.

18. The telegraph was invented by ______________________

19. The Apache leader who held out longest against the United States government was

____

Name ______________________________ Date ________________

20. How did the telegraph compare to the Pony Express as a means of cross-country communication?

____

21. What important event in American history happened at Promontory Point, Utah, on May 10, 1869?

____

22. Why did the Texas cattle industry grow after 1867?

____

____

23. Why did the U.S. government force the Plains Indians onto reservations?

____

____

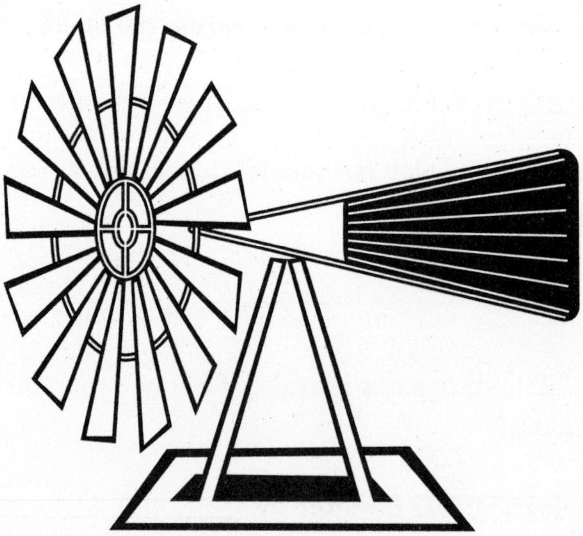

24. Look at the picture. What did farmers use that object for?

____

25. How did the price of wheat influence farmers to join the Grange?

____

Name ______________________________ Date ________________

Use what you have learned about comparing information from maps and graphs to answer questions 26-28.

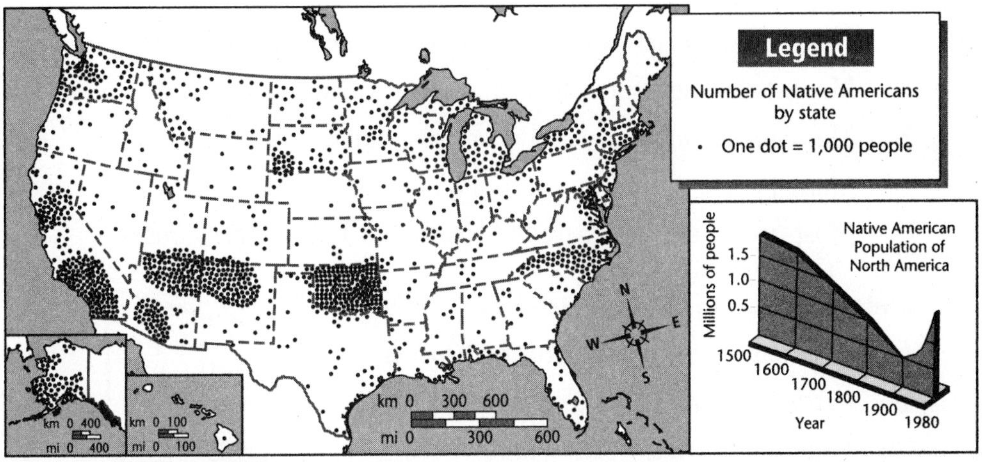

26. **What is the MAIN idea of the information in the map?**

____

____

27. **What is the MAIN idea of the information in the graph?**

____

____

28. **Compare the map and the graph. What does the graph show that the map does not? What does the map show that the graph does not?**

____

____

____

Name ______________________ Date ______________

Chapter 19 Test

Choose the best answer. Circle the letter next to your choice.

1. How did the Industrial Revolution affect where people lived?

A. Many people left rural areas and went to cities.
B. Many people left cities and went to suburbs.
C. Many people moved to the countryside to work on farms.
D. Most people stayed where they were, but built bigger houses.

2. Andrew Carnegie became rich by —

A. inventing a new manufacturing process
B. starting a company in a new industry
C. being born into a wealthy family
D. building libraries and universities

3. At immigration stations in New York and San Francisco in the late 1800s, immigrants —

A. were examined by doctors and questioned by officials
B. received several weeks of lessons in the English language
C. were tested on their knowledge of American history
D. had to prove they had relatives in the United States

4. In the late 1800s and the early 1900s, American cities became crowded because —

A. people preferred living in the newly built tenements
B. immigrants and rural people came to cities to look for jobs
C. immigrants took farm jobs so rural people came to the cities
D. people from the suburbs moved to cities to be near entertainment

5. What working conditions did workers usually find in factories and mines in the late 1800s?

A. Mechanization made their jobs easier and more satisfying.
B. Workplaces were safe and conditions were good.
C. The hours were long, and conditions were often dangerous.
D. Government rules limited the workday to eight hours.

Name ______________________________ Date ________________

6. In the late 1800s and early 1900s, many workers went on strike MAINLY to obtain —

A. a voice in running the company

B. machines that made their work easier

C. ownership of businesses

D. better wages and working conditions

7. For many years, most Americans thought Alaska was a worthless piece of frozen land. What changed their opinion?

A. The climate changed.

B. Gold was discovered.

C. Naval bases were needed for the Spanish-American War.

D. New inventions made Alaskan agriculture possible.

8. What new territory did the United States gain as a result of the Spanish-American war?

A. Cuba and Panama

B. Southern California

C. Texas

D. Puerto Rico and the Philippines

9. Who was the labor leader who became the first president of the American Federation of Labor?

A. Jane Addams

B. Andrew Carnegie

C. Samuel Gompers

D. Thomas Edison

10. When industry expanded in the United States in the late 1800s, what effect did it have on immigration?

A. Immigration increased because immigrants came to find work.

B. Immigration decreased because mechanization meant fewer jobs for immigrants.

C. Immigration increased because people who were born in the United States were not allowed to work in factories.

D. Immigration was not affected by expanding industry.

Name ______________________________ Date ____________________

For questions 11–15, choose the term from the list below that matches the description. Write the term in the space provided.

mechanization	**pogrom**	**yellow journalism**	**strike**
entrepreneur	**settlement house**	**monopoly**	

11. refusing to work ______________________________

12. someone who starts a business, hoping to make a profit

____

13. a business that controls all aspects of a particular industry

____

14. reporting stories in an exaggerated or untruthful manner

____

15. machines performing the jobs that people once did

____

Answer questions 16–25 in the spaces provided. Continue your answer on the back of the sheet if you need to.

16. In the late 1880s, what American symbol for freedom did immigrants pass by when they entered New York harbor?

____

17. The telephone was invented in 1876 by ______________________________

18. How did the Bessemer process change transportation?

____

____

Name ______________________________ Date ________________

19. In the late 1800s, a number of people became very wealthy as entrepreneurs. What attitudes and personality might a successful entrepreneur have?

____

20. How did public schools help immigrant children adjust to their new country?

____

21. Why did many immigrants tend to live in ethnic neighborhoods?

____

____

22. Was it possible for a child your age to work in a factory in the 1800s? Explain why or why not.

____

____

23. Why are workers joined together in a labor union more likely to be successful in asking an employer for a change than individual workers would be?

____

____

24. What happened when Queen Liliuokalani tried to take power back from the sugar and pineapple planters in Hawaii?

____

25. How did the Spanish-American War help make the United States a world power?

____

Name ______________________ Date ______________

In this chapter, you have learned about interpreting political cartoons. Use what you have learned to answer questions 26–28. The cartoon shown below was drawn by Thomas Nast and published on April 1, 1882. He is commenting about the United States' policy toward Chinese immigrants. The man on the left, carrying a bundle, represents those immigrants. "The Temple of Liberty" represents the United States.

April 1, 1882

E Pluribus Unum (Except the Chinese).

26. **Do the entrance and guards look welcoming or threatening? Explain.**

____

27. **"E Pluribus Unum" means "one from many" and indicates that the United States is made up of many cultures. What does Nast mean by "E Pluribus Unum (Except the Chinese)"?**

____

28. **What point of view is the artist trying to show about the United States' policy toward Chinese immigrants?**

____

Name ______________________________ Date ________________

Open-ended Response

In the second half of the nineteenth century, the United States changed in many ways. Railroads crossed the continent, industries grew, immigrants arrived. The lives of many people changed. Change can be exciting, but it can also be hard to cope with. Often people find strength by banding together.

Choose one group of people whose lives changed. Use what you have learned in this unit to explain how those people coped with the changes in their lives. You might write a paragraph or a news story, or create a "before and after" diagram.

Use the lines below for your notes. Prepare your response on separate sheets.

Theme Project Rubric

Use this scoring rubric for a holistic assessment of each student's work on the Theme Project, "Changing Times," on page 477 of the Student Book. You might begin by reviewing the entirety of a student's work and deciding *in general* which description most closely fits the work being evaluated. For example, you might decide that a product could *best* be described, in general, by the level 4 rubric than by the level 3.

Level 4	Level 3	Level 2	Level 1
• The project demonstrates thorough and in-depth knowledge of the technological, economic, and social transformation of the United States in the late 1800s. • The project includes many of the following: a map, an editorial, and diagrams or drawings. • The project analyzes technological change and social attitudes and customs and maintains a consistent point of view. • Materials are clear and well-organized and show evidence of planning and attention to detail. • The project reflects detailed research and synthesis of information and uses visuals effectively.	• The project demonstrates knowledge of the technological, economic, and social transformation of the United States in the late 1800s. • The project includes several types of work, such as a map, an editorial, and diagrams or drawings. • The project analyzes one technological change and some social attitudes and customs, establishes a point of view, and draws logical conclusions. • Maps, drawings, and writing are mostly clear, appropriately labeled, and well-organized; writing errors do not detract from content. • The work reflects research and synthesis of information and uses visuals appropriately.	• The project demonstrates some misunderstandings of the technological, economic, and/or social transformation of the United States in the late 1800s. • The project includes only one or two types of work or some work that does not relate directly to the post-Civil War period. • The project needs revising to analyze technological change and social attitudes and customs, establish a point of view, and exclude inappropriate materials. • The materials need a consistent organization scheme and have many writing errors. Maps and drawings are difficult to interpret. • The project demonstrates distinct deficiencies in research skills.	• The project shows fundamental misunderstandings of the technological, economic, and social transformation of the United States in the late 1800s. • The project fails in significant ways to meet the assignment. • There is little evidence of analysis, understanding point of view, or supporting logical arguments. • The materials are difficult to read; no organization is apparent. Maps and visuals are missing or features are not recognizable. • The project provides little or no evidence of research skills.

Name ______________________________ Date ________________

Performance Assessment Event

Your teacher will give you directions for using this page.

In this unit, you have learned about the United States in the late 1800s when people were coping with change. One kind of change came from technology. New inventions changed people's lives, in both good and bad ways. Some inventions from this period are listed below.

barbed wire	**telegraph**	**telephone**
Bessemer process	**light bulb**	**sewing machine**
typewriter	**elevator**	

Choose one of these inventions or another invention from the same period in history. Make a poster that shows the invention and what it does. On the poster, list the changes caused by the invention. Put the good changes in one column. If there are any bad changes, list them in another column. At the bottom of the poster, write a conclusion, explaining how the invention changed the United States.

Your poster will be evaluated according to these criteria:

1. Does the poster show what an invention does?
2. Does the poster show the changes caused by the invention?
3. Does the conclusion explain how the invention changed the United States?

Extensions

A. Choose a 20th century invention such as television, compact discs, or the computer. Work with other students to present a panel discussion about that invention and its effects, both good and bad. Each student on the panel will discuss one topic relating to the invention.

Your panel discussion will be judged according to the following criteria:

1. accuracy and completeness of information
2. ease in following presentation
3. style and organization of presentation
4. participation of all panel members

B. Make a timeline for inventions. Discuss which invention has had the greatest effect.

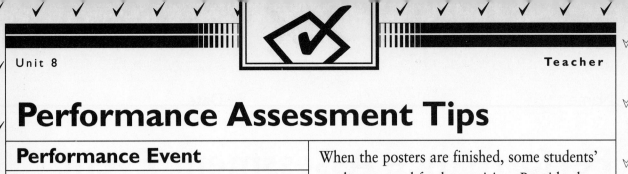

Performance Assessment Tips

Performance Event

If your students have completed the Theme Project for Unit 8, suggest that they review the research they did on inventions and the before-and-after diagrams they prepared. Review the communicative purpose of a poster. Point out the importance of clarity and visual appeal. Emphasize the importance of the conclusion section of this poster.

Help students prepare a resource table with information on the history of technology. Include books about technology and inventions, as well as students' theme projects.

Have students who are interested in a particular invention form small groups to discuss that invention and its effects. Suggest that students plan the poster by making a sketch and by writing a rough draft of statements.

As students complete their sketches, have them check their work to be sure that it is accurate and contains the required elements. Have students work with a peer to revise their sketches and drafts.

When the posters are finished, some students' work may need further revision. Provide clear directions for those students. For example, if they need to add more effects, help them determine where they might find information they need.

For students who must begin over again, have them look at some excellent posters as models. Discuss what makes the posters excellent. Have students write an outline of their points. After you approve the outline, they can begin work on the poster.

Extensions

A. Explain how to organize a panel discussion. Help students decide how to divide topics among panelists. Topics might be divided as follows: a description of the invention and what it does; its good effects; its bad effects; how it changed life in the United States.

B. The invention timeline might be a collaborative activity for small groups or the class as a whole. First, students need to decide the time span that the timeline will cover. Then they can choose the inventions to show on the timeline and do research to learn when each invention was developed. They might illustrate the timeline with pictures of the inventions.

Performance Assessment Rubric

Use this scoring rubric for a holistic assessment of each student's work on the Performance Assessment Event on page 133 of *Assessment Options*. You might begin by reviewing the entirety of a student's work and deciding *in general* which description most closely fits the work being evaluated. For example, you might decide that a product could *best* be described, in general, by the level 4 rubric rather than the level 3.

Level 4	Level 3	Level 2	Level 1
• The poster shows substantial knowledge of a specific invention. • The poster shows the invention's effects, both positive and negative. A conclusion is drawn. • Cause and effect relationships are clearly drawn. Effects are correct and show research and/or creative thinking. • The conclusion drawn is logical. • Material is well-presented and easy to follow. • The poster shows excellent application of such social studies skills as seeing cause-effect relationships, drawing conclusions, creating visual materials, and using source materials.	• The poster shows knowledge of a specific invention. • The poster shows the invention and some of its effects. A conclusion is drawn. • Cause and effect relationships are present but not entirely clear. Effects are generally correct. The conclusion is logical. • The material is easy to follow, but there are some errors. • The material shows the use of social studies skills such as seeing cause-effect relationships, drawing conclusions, creating visual materials, and using source materials.	• The poster shows knowledge of a specific invention, but minor errors may be present. • The poster shows only some effects. The conclusion may be missing. • Cause and effect relationships are not clear. Effects are frequently incorrect. The conclusion is missing or illogical. • The material is not easy to follow due to errors. • There is evidence of the application of relevant social studies skills. Some weakness in skills is apparent.	• The poster shows little understanding of an invention. • Only a few effects are covered. No conclusion is drawn. • The material shows little or no evidence of sound thinking skills. • An audience would have difficulty understanding the poster. • Use of relevant social studies skills is not evident.

Name ______________________ Date ______________

Chapter 20 Test

Choose the best answer. Circle the letter next to your choice.

1. What was one result of Upton Sinclair's book *The Jungle*?

A. Teddy Roosevelt was elected President.

B. Working conditions improved in most factories.

C. Congress passed laws regulating the food industry.

D. Laws were passed limiting the hours children could work.

2. What did women and African Americans achieve during the Progressive era?

A. They each formed groups to seek their own legal rights.

B. They focused the country's attention on World War I.

C. They gained equal pay and better working conditions.

D. They gained full legal and economic equality.

3. What event immediately followed the sinking of the Lusitania?

A. The United States joined the Central Powers.

B. People in the United States voted for a new President.

C. France entered the war on the side of the British.

D. American public opinion turned against Germany.

4. What role did the United States play in World War I?

A. It was neutral all through the war.

B. It gave the Allies a military advantage by joining their side.

C. It gave the Central powers a military advantage by joining their side.

D. It switched sides halfway through the war.

5. What was an initial effect of the assembly line on the American economy?

A. New products became available to more Americans.

B. It did not have any effect.

C. More workers were needed to produce products.

D. Products took longer to build and were more expensive.

Name ______________________________ Date ____________________

6. **What did FDR's New Deal do to improve conditions during the Great Depression?**
   A. It gave money to banks so they could reopen.
   B. It relocated farmers from the Plains states to California.
   C. It gave money to businesses so they could pay their employees.
   D. It created government agencies that put people back to work.

7. **President Roosevelt called December 7, 1941, "a day which will live in infamy." What happened on that day?**
   A. Japanese-Americans were sent to internment camps.
   B. Japanese planes attacked Pearl Harbor.
   C. Adolph Hitler became head of the Nazi Party.
   D. The United States dropped an atomic bomb on Hiroshima.

8. **What did the Allies do to push Germany out of France in World War II?**
   A. They liberated the concentration camps.
   B. They forced Hitler out of power.
   C. They invaded Normandy.
   D. They dropped an atomic bomb on Paris.

9. **What happened when men left factory jobs to join the armed forces during World War II?**
   A. Factories were forced to close because they had no workers.
   B. Women took factory jobs to make weapons for the war.
   C. Factories replaced the workers with machines.
   D. Japanese-Americans were forced to work in the factories.

Name ______________________ Date ______________

10. Use the timeline below and your knowledge of American history to decide which event belongs on the X on the timeline.

A. the end of World War I B. D-Day
C. the stock market crash D. the election of Woodrow Wilson

For questions 11–15, choose the term from the list below that matches the description. Write the term in the space provided.

muckrakers	**Holocaust**	**armistice**
Axis Powers	**stock market**	**Allied Powers**

11. people who search for and expose corruption ______________________

12. the mass murder by the Nazis of 11 million men, women, and children

____

13. a halt in fighting ______________________

14. a place where people buy and sell shares in a company ______________________

15. the combined forces of Germany, Italy, and Japan during World War II

____

For questions 16 and 17, answer each question in the space provided.

16. Who was W.E.B. Dubois and what was he famous for? ______________________

____

17. What organization was established by the Treaty of Versailles in 1918 to help countries keep peace with one another?

____

Name ______________________________ Date ____________________

Write the answers for questions 18–25 in the space below each question. Continue on to the back of the sheet if you need to.

18. In the early 1900s, what was the Progressives' view on the role of government?

____

19. If the women who worked at the Triangle Shirtwaist Factory could have voted, what sort of laws would they probably have been in favor of?

____

20. What do you think President Wilson meant when he called World War I "the war to end all wars"?

____

21. Explain how the arrival of American soldiers affected the outcome of World War I.

____

22. How did new modes of communication in the Roaring Twenties change American life?

____

23. What did Franklin Delano Roosevelt mean when he said in 1933, "The only thing we have to fear is fear itself"?

____

24. How did the treaty that ended World War I relate to the rise of Adolph Hitler?

____

25. In your opinion, did President Truman do the right thing when he decided to use the atomic bomb in Japan? Be sure to give a reason for your opinion.

____

Name ______________________ Date ______________

You have learned about interpreting the information in line graphs. Use your skills to answer questions 26–28.

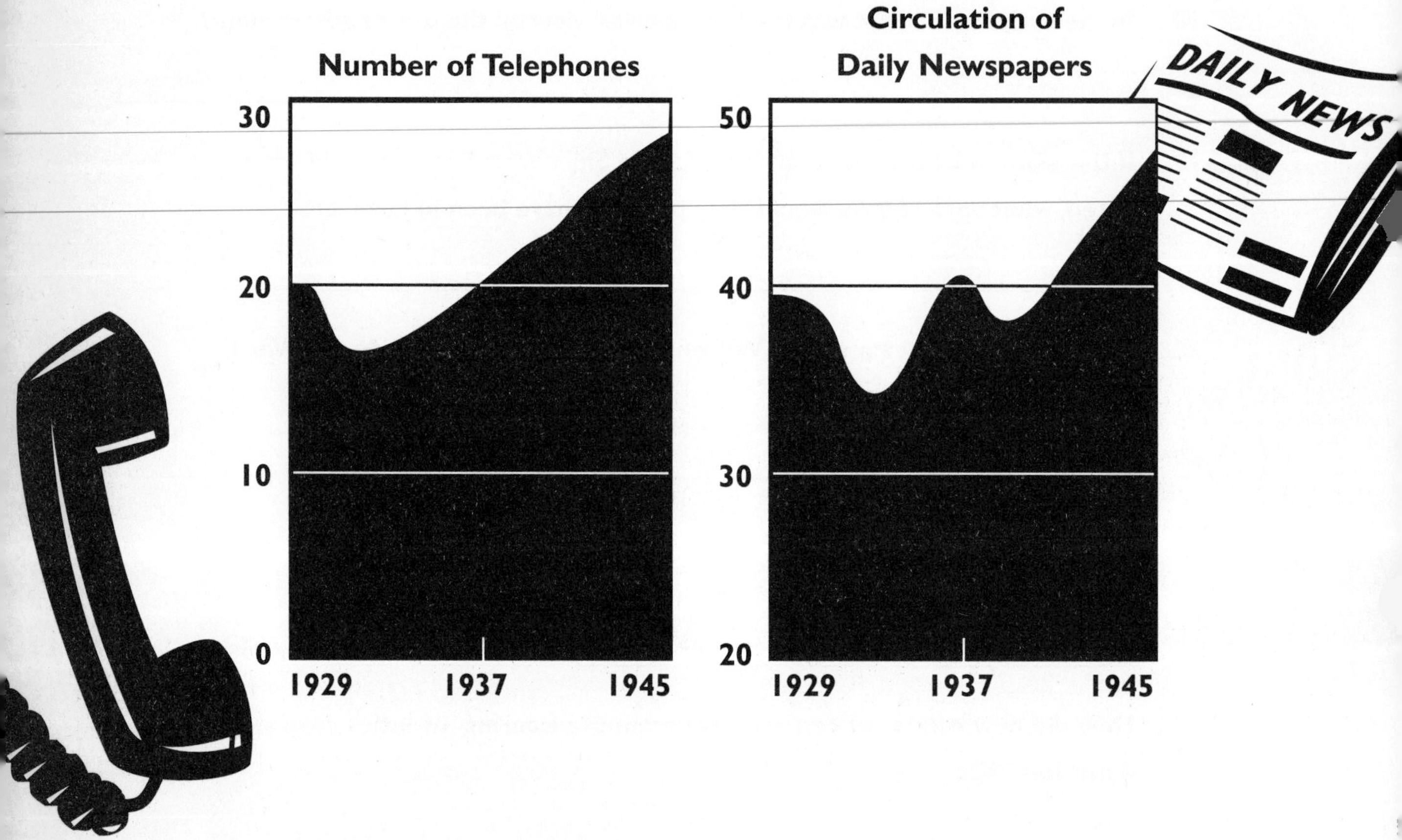

26. What kind of information is in each graph?

____

27. Is the trend shown in the two graphs similar for the period from 1929 to the early 1930s? Explain your answer.

____

28. Compare the data in the graphs for the period from 1937 to 1945. What trends do you see? What conditions probably account for the trends?

____

Name ______________________ Date ______________

Chapter 21 Test

Choose the best answer. Circle the letter next to your choice.

1. **How did the United States and the Soviet Union fight the Cold War?**
   A. They used "superbombs" in Korea.
   B. They fought battles in Europe along the Iron Curtain.
   C. They used new weapons on each other's territory.
   D. They raced to build bigger, stronger weapons.

2. **During the 1950s, the lives of many American families were changed by the arrival of —**
   A. television
   B. personal computers
   C. shopping malls
   D. radio

3. **In the early 1950s, there were laws about public education in 17 states that —**
   A. provided extra money for schools with many immigrant children
   B. required African American children and white children to go to different schools
   C. let children travel to school free on city buses
   D. required all children to attend the school that was geographically closest to their home

4. **What did the Civil Rights Act of 1964 accomplish?**
   A. It guaranteed the policy of "separate but equal."
   B. It promised jobs to all citizens.
   C. It made segregation illegal.
   D. It provided equal funds for all public schools.

Name ____________________ Date ____________

5. The MAIN reason that the United States sent troops first to South Korea and then to South Vietnam was that the United States wanted to —

A. protect American citizens living in those countries

B. be sure that oil resources in both countries were safe

C. stop the spread of Communism

D. respond to attacks on American bases

6. Communism is a political and economic system in which most businesses are owned and run by —

A. people elected by local workers

B. private enterprise

C. the government

D. a political party

7. What have groups such as the UFW, AIM, and NOW worked to do in America over the last 30 years?

A. increase fair treatment of minority groups

B. lower taxes and increase profits

C. end the Cold War

D. improve the economy

8. American students can follow President Kennedy's advice to do something for their country by —

A. waiting patiently until they are old enough to vote

B. accepting whatever government officials say and do

C. hoping that other people will help them first

D. getting involved in their school and community

Name ______________________________ Date ____________________

This timeline shows some events of the Cold War and the Civil Rights movement. Use it to help you answer questions 9 and 10.

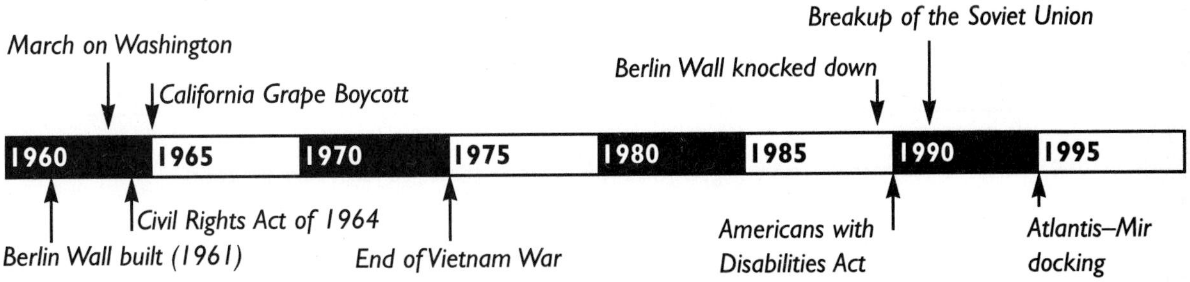

9. The knocking down of the Berlin Wall signaled —

A. the end of the Cold War

B. the success of protests against the war in Vietnam

C. the end of the Korean War

D. Yeltsin's election as Russia's president

10. What was the relationship between the March on Washington and the Civil Rights Act?

A. The march was called to celebrate the passage of the Civil Rights Act.

B. The march was a message that it was time to pass the Civil Rights Act.

C. The Civil Rights Act made it legal to have the march.

D. The march was a protest against the passage of the Civil Rights Act.

Answer questions 11–19 in the spaces provided. Continue your answer on the back of the sheet if you need to.

11. In 1954, in the case of *Brown v. the Board of Education of Topeka,* the Supreme Court outlawed

____

12. In 1952, the United States exploded its first ____________________

13. Explain the term *Iron Curtain.* ______________________________

____

Name ______________________________ Date ________________

14. How was the "baby boom" linked to higher paychecks and high hopes for the future?

____

____

15. List TWO ways that segregation laws affected African Americans.

____

____

16. During the 1950s and 1960s, African Americans protested unfair treatment in a number of ways. List TWO things people did as nonviolent protests.

____

____

17. Television brought the Vietnam War into homes across the country. How did television affect people's opinions about the war?

____

____

18. Explain the contributions of TWO of the following groups: the United Farm Workers, the American Indian Movement, and the National Organization for Women.

____

____

19. What are two goals the United States and Russia achieved by working together?

____

____

Name ______________________________ Date ____________________

For questions 20–24, choose the term from the list below that matches the description. Write the term in the space provided

capitalism	**communism**	**Peace Corps**	**suburb**
docked	**arms race**	**civil rights**	**migrant worker**

20. fair and equal treatment under the Constitution ____________________

21. a person who moves from place to place looking for farm work ____________

22. volunteers helping people in developing nations in such areas as education, agriculture, and small business

____

23. a race to build bigger, stronger weapons ____________________

24. an area outside of a city designed just for homes ____________________

Use the oral history skills you have learned to answer questions 25–27.

What if you could interview a person who had joined the March on Washington in August, 1963, and heard Martin Luther King, Jr., speak?

25. What sources of information would be good to look at to prepare for your interview?

____

____

26. What would be TWO good questions to ask during the interview?

____

____

27. List THREE things you should do after the interview.

____

____

Name ______________________ Date ______________

Chapter 22 Test

Choose the best answer. Circle the letter next to your choice.

1. Canada's resources of trees, petroleum, and good farmland are MOSTLY located —

A. near the St. Lawrence Seaway
B. in the Appalachian Highlands
C. in the far northern part of the country
D. in western Canada

2. What is the MAIN economic role of the St. Lawrence Seaway?

A. It gives inland Canada a water route to world markets.
B. It provides electric power to manufacture goods in eastern cities.
C. It provides water to irrigate farmland.
D. It creates recreational opportunities and attracts tourists.

3. Canada is mostly a nation of immigrants. Canada's form of parliamentary government is part of Canada's heritage from —

A. France
B. the United States
C. Britain
D. China

4. Why do some Quebecois want to separate from English-speaking Canada?

A. to become part of the United States
B. to take more advantage of the natural resources of Quebec
C. to form a special trade relationship with France
D. to become an independent nation

Name ______________________________ Date ____________________

5. Much of Mexico's best farmland is in the largest physical region in Mexico. This region is called the —

A. Pacific Northwest
B. Central Plateau
C. Gulf Coastal Plain
D. Yucatán Peninsula

6. If a scientific team wanted to study tropical rain forests in Mexico, they would probably go to the —

A. Pacific Northwest
B. Central Plateau
C. Gulf Coastal Plain
D. Yucatán Peninsula

7. Which of the following statements best describes Mexican culture today?

A. Mexican culture is a blend of Native American and Spanish cultures.
B. African and Asian cultures have shaped modern Mexican culture.
C. Mexican culture today combines cultures from Canada and Europe.
D. Spain provided both the language and the culture of Mexico.

8. Based on the average age of the Mexican population today, one of the biggest future challenges will be —

A. finding new deposits of oil
B. building railroads and airports
C. creating jobs
D. expanding agriculture

9. The goal of the North American Free Trade Agreement is to increase trade among the United States, Mexico, and Canada by —

A. building roads to transport goods
B. gradually ending tariffs
C. putting high taxes on goods from other countries
D. sponsoring student exchanges

Name ______________________________ Date ________________

10. How has trade among the nations of the Americas changed today?

A. The nations of the Americas trade only with Europe.
B. The nations of the Americas are just beginning to trade with each other.
C. There is more trade among the nations of the Americas than ever before.
D. Trade among the nations of the Americas has dropped sharply.

11. People throughout the hemisphere work toward common goals through different grassroots organizations. These organizations are made up of —

A. government officials only
B. ordinary citizens
C. elected delegates
D. business executives

12. What is ONE major goal of the Organization of American States?

A. to create grassroots organizations
B. to increase trade between American nations
C. to find new crops that will grow in the Western Hemisphere
D. to call for higher tariffs between member countries

For questions 13–17, choose the term from the list below that matches the description. Write the term in the space provided.

petrodollar	**tariff**	**trading partner**	**province**
infrastructure	**grassroots**	**Canadian Shield**	**standard of living**
bilingual			

13. having two official languages ______________________

14. money earned from selling oil ______________________

15. a country's system of transportation and communications

____

16. an extra tax on goods brought into a country ______________________

17. a rock formation that covers much of eastern Canada

____

Name ______________________________ Date ________________

Directions: For questions 18–19, choose the appropriate letter on the map.

18. Which letter marks the location of Québec?

____

19. Which letter marks the location of Mexico City?

____

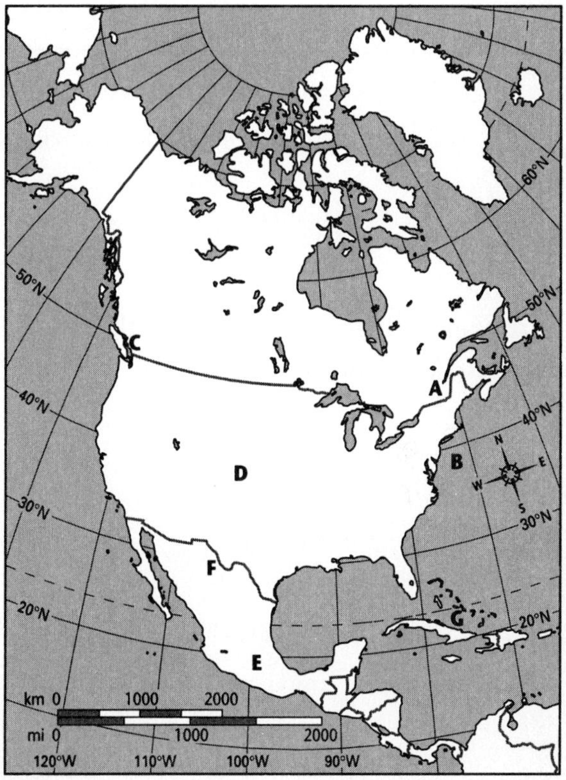

Answer questions 20–25 in the spaces provided. Continue your answer on the back of the sheet if you need to.

20. Jacques Cartier said he could not see "a cartload of dirt" in Quebec. What didn't he know about Canada's resources?

____

21. What does it mean to call Canada a mosaic society?

____

22. Where are Mexico's mountains located? What effect have Mexico's mountains had on the country's development?

____

23. What effect did the discovery of oil in the 1970s have on Mexico's economy?

____

Name ______________________________ Date ____________________

24. What are some advantages of free trade?

____

25. Describe how grassroots organizations are important in improving health and education in the Americas.

____

Directions: These two maps show the world in different perspectives. Use your map skills to answer questions 26–29.

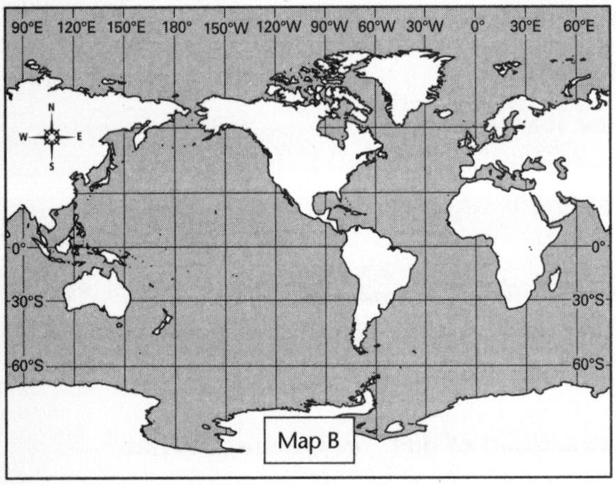

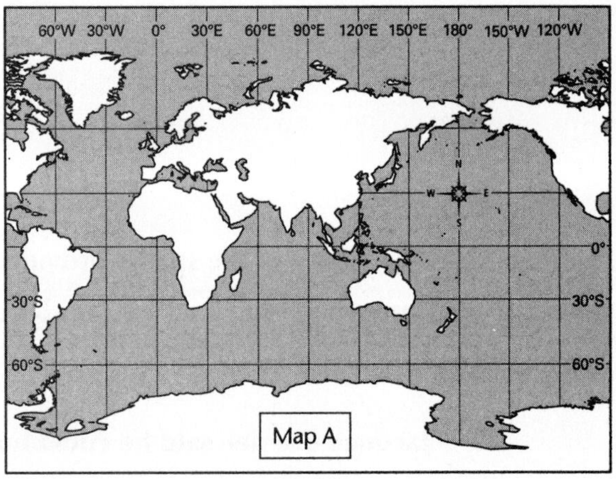

26. Which hemisphere is at the center of Map A?

____

27. Which hemisphere is at the center of Map B?

____

28. Why is the United States cut in half on Map A?

____

29. Which map are you more used to? Why do you think you have seen this map more often?

____

Name ______________________ Date ______________

Open-ended Response

In the twentieth century, the United States has had many challenges to cope with, from fighting for freedom abroad to protecting American citizens at home. The timeline below shows some major events of the twentieth century.

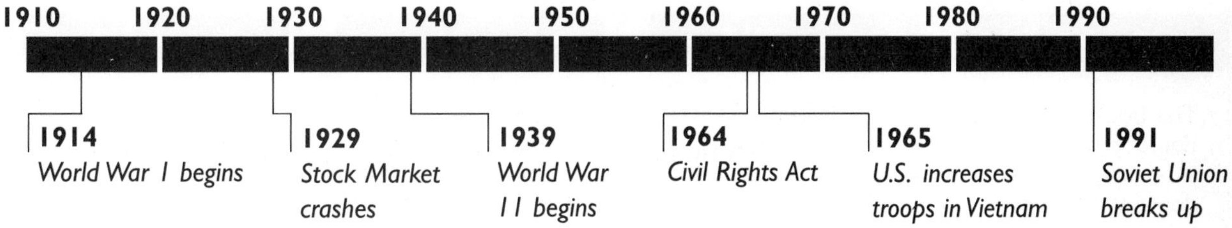

Which event in the twentieth century has had an effect on your life or that of somebody in your family? Use an event on the timeline or choose some other event. Tell what the event was and explain why it was a challenge.

Use the lines below for your notes. Prepare your response on separate sheets.

Theme Project Rubric

Use this scoring rubric for a holistic assessment of each student's work on the Theme Project, "The 20th Century," on page 531 of the Student Book. You might begin by reviewing the entirety of a student's work and deciding *in general* which description most closely fits the work being evaluated. For example, you might decide that a product could *best* be described, in general, by the level 4 rubric than by the level 3.

Level 4	Level 3	Level 2	Level 1
• The booth demonstrate thorough and in-depth knowledge of key people, events, and trends of one decade of the 20th century. • The booth includes many of the following: illustrations, a chart, music, and flyers. • The booth is clearly designed for an informative purpose; it analyzes events, evaluates key features, and creatively extends this knowledge. • Materials are clear and well-organized and show evidence of planning and attention to detail. • The booth reflects detailed research and synthesis of information and uses visuals effectively.	• The booth demonstrates knowledge of key people, events, and trends of one decade of the twentieth century. • The booth includes several types of work, such as maps, illustrations, music, speeches, flyers, and interviews. • The booth is mostly designed for an informative purpose; it analyzes and evaluates key events and people. • Maps, drawings, and writing are mostly clear, appropriately labeled, and well-organized; writing errors do not detract from content. • The booth reflects research and synthesis of information and uses visuals appropriately.	• The booth demonstrates some misunderstandings of events and trends of one decade of the twentieth century. • The booth includes only one or two types of work or some work that does not relate directly to the decade chosen. • The booth lacks an informative purpose and offers little analysis or evaluation of people and events. • The materials need a consistent organization scheme and have many writing errors. Maps and drawings are difficult to interpret. • The materials demonstrate distinct deficiencies in research and/or visual skills.	• The materials demonstrate a fundamental misunderstanding of key people, events, and trends of the twentieth century. • The materials presented fail in significant ways to meet the assignment. • The purpose of the booth is unclear. There is little evidence of analysis or evaluation. • The materials are difficult to read; no organization is evident. Visuals are missing or features are not recognizable. • The materials provide little or no evidence of research or visual skills.

Name ______________________ Date ______________

Performance Assessment Event

Your teacher will give you directions for using this page.

In this unit, you have learned about the United States in the twentieth century. You have seen how our country has fought for freedom all over the world and taken more responsibility for helping its citizens.

For this event, you will use what you have learned to prepare questions for a game show. You will write 10 questions, one for each decade.

1900-1909	1950-1959
1910-1919	1960-1969
1920-1929	1970-1979
1930-1939	1980-1989
1940-1949	1990-1999

Questions can come from the categories below. In the ten questions that you write, you should use at least four of the five categories.

Famous Faces — Find the Place
Important Dates — Name the Tune
Important Objects and Inventions

Write each question on one side of an index card. At the top of the card, write the decade, the category, and your name. On the other side, write the answer and how you checked to be sure the answer was correct.
(You can check in your textbook, encyclopedias, or other reference books.)

Here is what your teacher will look for in evaluating the cards:

1. Do your questions and answers show that you know a lot about the 20th century?
2. Do your questions cover all the decades and at least four categories?
3. Do they ask for interesting and important information? Did you write the source of the information?
4. Are the questions clearly written?

Extensions

A. Play the game in teams. Sort questions by decade or by category. You can create rules for playing the game or use a format like a game show on television.

Your team's performance will be judged according to the the following criteria:

1. accuracy of answers
2. participation of all team members

B. Collect all the cards in the class and sort them according to category. Then the class should divide into five groups, one for each category. Students in each group should work together to find the answers to all the questions in the category.

Performance Assessment Tips

Performance Event

If your students have completed the Theme Project for Unit 9, encourage them to review the materials they prepared, paying particular attention to material that would make good questions. Point out classroom maps and other visual materials that could be used to prompt questions. If possible, have both U.S. and world maps put up in the classroom during this performance assessment.

Have students create a resource table to use in creating questions. Possible resources include music cassettes, almanacs, reference books, timelines, and so on. Adults who remember particular decades can also provide resource material, such as old newspapers, photographs, and mementos.

Students may want to brainstorm in small groups. Suggest that they concentrate either on a particular decade or a particular category.

As students complete questions, have them work in pairs to check questions for clarity. After you evaluate students' work, you might want some students to revise or rethink their projects. Have students correct content errors first, and then correct writing errors. If some cards are correct, students need only revise incorrect cards. For students who must re-do most of their cards, have them look at some excellent cards as a model. It may help students to break the task into smaller pieces. For example, you might tell them to write one question and answer about a famous person who lived in the 1980s. Then they can go on to other decades and categories.

Extensions

A. Assign a group of students to formulate rules for the game, including scoring. The rules should be written out. Check to make sure that all students understand the rules before play begins. Each team should be made up of some students who know the unit's content very well and others who are less proficient.

B. Provide reference materials to help students find the answers to the questions in the categories. When the groups have finished, they might pool all their answers into a fact-file book on the 20th century.

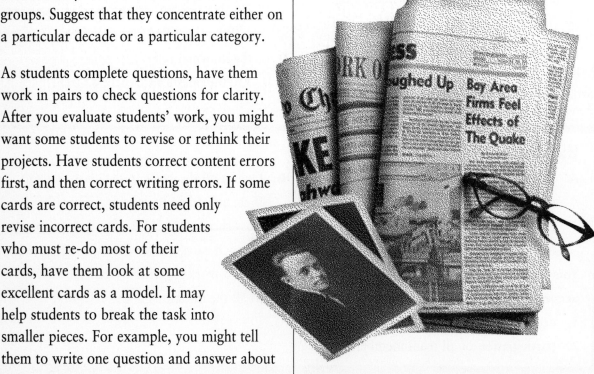

Performance Assessment Rubric

Use this scoring rubric for a holistic assessment of each student's work on the Performance Assessment Event on page 153 of *Assessment Options*. You might begin by reviewing the entirety of a student's work and deciding *in general* which description most closely fits the work being evaluated. For example, you might decide that a product could *best* be described, in general, by the level 4 rubric rather than the level 3.

Level 4

- The questions and answers show substantial knowledge of the people, places, dates, and events of the twentieth century.
- Questions cover all decades and categories. Answers are correct and contain source information.
- The questions cover interesting and important information. Material has been correctly classified.
- Questions and answers are well-worded and clearly written.
- The questions and answers show excellent application of such social studies skills as using source materials, understanding historical periods, and analyzing information.

Level 3

- The questions and answers show knowledge of the people, places, dates, and events of the twentieth century, but minor errors may be present.
- Questions cover all decades and four categories. Answers are generally correct and usually contain source information.
- Most questions cover interesting and important information. Material has been correctly classified.
- Questions and answers are are generally easy to follow.
- The material shows adequate use of social studies skills such as using source materials, understanding historical periods, and analyzing information.

Level 2

- The questions and answers demonstrate weak knowledge of the people, places, dates, and events of the twentieth century. There are errors or omissions in content.
- Only some of the decades and categories are covered. Some answers are incorrect or missing source information.
- Questions are often trivial or illogical. There are errors in classification.
- The wording of questions is difficult to follow.
- There is some evidence of the application of relevant social studies skills. Some weakness in skills is apparent.

Level I

- The questions and answers show little understanding of he people, places, dates, and events of the twentieth century.
- Only a few decades and categories are covered. Many answers are incorrect. Source material is not included.
- Most questions are trivial, illogical, or irrelevant.
- An audience would have difficulty understanding the questions and answers.
- Use of relevant social studies skills is not evident.

Group members ______________________ Date ______________

Evaluation

Cooperative Groups

Project ____

Objective ____

Rate each element of group work on the basis of the following scale:

4 = Excellent 3 = Very Good 2 = Acceptable 1 = Needs Improvement

	Rating (circle one)			
1. The group understood its objective.	**4**	**3**	**2**	**1**
2. The group remained focused on its objective.	**4**	**3**	**2**	**1**
3. The group managed its time well.	**4**	**3**	**2**	**1**
4. The group accomplished its goal.	**4**	**3**	**2**	**1**
5. Members understood their roles and responsibilities within the group.	**4**	**3**	**2**	**1**
6. Members listened to one another with attention and respect.	**4**	**3**	**2**	**1**
7. Members strived to work out differences.	**4**	**3**	**2**	**1**

Overall Evaluation

8. What did the group do best?

____

____

9. What would help the group work better?

____

____

Name ______________________________ Date ________________

Self-Assessment

Group Work

Answer these questions about the group project.

1. **Who were the members?** ____________________

2. **What was the goal?** ____________________

3. **Did the group accomplish its goal? (check one)**

   ○ Yes ○ No

   Explanation ____________________

   ____

Put a check next to the word that best describes each statement.

4. **I understood my role in the group.**

   ○ Always ○ Sometimes ○ Never

5. **I contributed my share to the group.**

   ○ Always ○ Sometimes ○ Never

6. **I listened closely to others without interrupting.**

   ○ Always ○ Sometimes ○ Never

7. **I respected other people's opinions, even when I disagreed with them.**

   ○ Always ○ Sometimes ○ Never

Complete these sentences about your work in the group.

8. **What I learned from this project is** ____________________

   ____

   ____

9. **What I might do differently next time I work with a group is** ____________________

   ____

   ____

Student ______________________ Date ______________

Evaluation

Oral Presentations

Assignment ______________________

Objective ______________________

Rate each element of the oral presentation according to this scale:

4 = Excellent 3 = Very Good 2 = Acceptable 1 = Needs Improvement

		Rating (circle one)			
1.	**You stated your topic and purpose clearly.**	**4**	**3**	**2**	**1**
2.	**You gathered and presented strong facts.**	**4**	**3**	**2**	**1**
3.	**You stayed on your topic.**	**4**	**3**	**2**	**1**
4.	**You showed an understanding of people, places, and events related to your topic.**	**4**	**3**	**2**	**1**
5.	**You organized facts in a way that suited your topic and was easy to follow.**	**4**	**3**	**2**	**1**
6.	**You distinguished between fact and opinion.**	**4**	**3**	**2**	**1**
7.	**Any visual aids you used were clear and helpful.**	**4**	**3**	**2**	**1**
8.	**You made eye contact with your audience and spoke clearly, loudly, and smoothly.**	**4**	**3**	**2**	**1**

Overall Evaluation

9. What I liked best was ______________________

____

____

10. Next time you should ______________________

____

____

Name ______________________ Date ______________

Peer Assessment

Oral Presentations

Answer these questions about the presentation you are evaluating.

1. **Which speaker are you evaluating?** ______________________
2. **What kind of presentation was it?** ______________________
3. **What was the topic?** ______________________
4. **What were the main points?** ______________________

____

Put a check next to the word that best describes each statement.

5. **The speaker kept to the topic.**
   ○ Always ○ Sometimes ○ Never
6. **The speaker presented enough facts to make his or her points clear and convincing.**
   ○ Always ○ Sometimes ○ Never
7. **The presentation was organized in a way that was easy to follow.**
   ○ Always ○ Sometimes ○ Never
8. **The speaker looked at the audience, spoke clearly, and could be heard easily.**
   ○ Always ○ Sometimes ○ Never

Complete these sentences to evaluate the presentation.

9. **Something I learned was** ______________________

____

10. **What I liked best was** ______________________

____

11. **Next time the speaker might want to** ______________________

____

Student ______________________________ Date ________________

Evaluation

Role-playing and Simulations

Assignment ____

Objective ____

Rate each element of the simulation according to this scale:

4 = Excellent   3 = Very Good   2 = Acceptable   1 = Needs Improvement

	Rating (circle one)			
1. You seemed to understand your role and stayed in it.	**4**	**3**	**2**	**1**
2. You showed an understanding of the people, places, and events involved.	**4**	**3**	**2**	**1**
3. You participated effectively in the conversations and actions.	**4**	**3**	**2**	**1**
4. You worked at reaching a conclusion that was logical.	**4**	**3**	**2**	**1**

Overall Evaluation

5. What I like best about your work is ____

____

____

6. Next time you should ____

____

____

Name ______________________ Date ______________

Peer Assessment

Role-playing and Simulations

Answer these questions about the simulation you are evaluating.

1. **Whom are you evaluating?** ______________________
2. **What is the topic?** ______________________
3. **What is the event?** ______________________
4. **Where and when does it take place?** ______________________

Which word best describes each statement? Put a check next to it.

5. **Group members were believable in their roles.**
   ○ Always ○ Sometimes ○ Never
6. **The group used background information to make the events seem real.**
   ○ Always ○ Sometimes ○ Never
7. **Group members participated effectively in the conversations and activities.**
   ○ Always ○ Sometimes ○ Never
8. **The group reached a reasonable and believable conclusion.**
   ○ Always ○ Sometimes ○ Never

Complete these sentences about the simulation.

9. **Something I learned was** ______________________

   ____

10. **What I liked best was** ______________________

    ____

11. **One thing the group might do differently next time is** ______________________

    ____

    ____

Group members ______________________ Date ______________

Evaluation

Visual Representations and Constructions (Group)

Assignment ______________________

Objective ______________________

Type of representation or construction ______________________

Rate each element of the group's work according to this scale:

4 = Excellent 3 = Very Good 2 = Acceptable 1 = Needs Improvement

	Rating (circle one)			
1. The work meets the goals of the assignment.	**4**	**3**	**2**	**1**
2. The group gathered and used appropriate information and material.	**4**	**3**	**2**	**1**
3. People, places, and events are depicted accurately.	**4**	**3**	**2**	**1**
4. The work shows an understanding of the geography, history, or culture.	**4**	**3**	**2**	**1**
5. The purpose comes across clearly.	**4**	**3**	**2**	**1**
6. The form and design fit the purpose.	**4**	**3**	**2**	**1**
7. There is evidence that everyone in the group did his or her share.	**4**	**3**	**2**	**1**

Overall Evaluation

8. The best part of the work is ______________________

____

9. Some things that might be improved are ______________________

____

____

Name ______________________ Date ______________

Self-Assessment

Visual Representations and Constructions (Group)

Answer these questions about your group.

1. The members of my group were ______________________

2. My group created ______________________

3. We tried to show ______________________

4. We had most difficulty with ______________________

Check the word that best tells how you feel about your work on this project.

5. I contributed my share.

○ Yes ○ No

6. I was satisfied with the result.

○ Yes ○ No

Answer these questions to evaluate the group project.

7. Did the group achieve its goal? (check one)

○ Yes ○ No ○ Partly

Explanation ______________________

____

8. From this project I learned ______________________

____

9. If I could work on another project like this, what I would do the same way is

____

____

10. What I would do differently is ______________________

____

Student ______________________________ Date ________________

Evaluation

Representations and Constructions (Individual)

Assignment ____

Objective ____

Type of representation or construction ____

4 = Excellent **3 = Very Good** **2 = Acceptable** **1 = Needs Improvement**

		Rating (circle one)			
1.	**You show details of people, places, and events correctly.**	**4**	**3**	**2**	**1**
2.	**You gathered and used appropriate information and material.**	**4**	**3**	**2**	**1**
3.	**Your work shows that you understand the geography, history, or culture involved.**	**4**	**3**	**2**	**1**
4.	**Your purpose comes across clearly.**	**4**	**3**	**2**	**1**
5.	**The form and design fit the purpose.**	**4**	**3**	**2**	**1**
6.	**Your work meets the goals of the assignment.**	**4**	**3**	**2**	**1**

Overall Evaluation

7. What I liked best was ____

____

____

8. Next time you might try ____

____

____

Name ______________________ Date ______________

Self-Assessment

Representations and Constructions (Individual)

Answer these questions about your work on the project.

1. **My assignment was** ______________________

2. **The visual form I used was** ______________________

3. **I tried to show** ______________________

____

4. **What was most difficult for me was** ______________________

____

5. **Do I think I fulfilled my goal? (check one)**

   ○ Yes ○ No

   Explanation ______________________

____

Complete these statements about your project.

6. **What I learned from working on this project is** ______________________

____

____

7. **What I like best about it is** ______________________

____

8. **What I like least about it is** ______________________

____

9. **If I could change it, I would** ______________________

Student ______________________________ Date ____________________

Evaluation

Map Making

Assignment ______________________________

Objective ______________________________

Rate each element of the map according to this scale:

4 = Excellent **3 = Very Good** **2 = Acceptable** **1 = Needs Improvement**

		Rating (circle one)			
1.	**You gave your map an appropriate title.**	**4**	**3**	**2**	**1**
2.	**Your information fits the purpose of the map.**	**4**	**3**	**2**	**1**
3.	**You included all the needed information.**	**4**	**3**	**2**	**1**
4.	**You showed the information accurately.**	**4**	**3**	**2**	**1**
5.	**You drew the outline accurately.**	**4**	**3**	**2**	**1**
6.	**You used appropriate and clear symbols and labels.**	**4**	**3**	**2**	**1**
7.	**You included an accurate compass rose and scale.**	**4**	**3**	**2**	**1**
8.	**The legend is complete and easy to read.**	**4**	**3**	**2**	**1**
9.	**Your map is clear and easy to follow.**	**4**	**3**	**2**	**1**

Overall Evaluation

10. What I like best about your map work is ______________________________

____

____

11. To improve your work, you might ______________________________

____

____

Name ______________________ Date ______________

Self-Assessment

Map Making

Complete these statements about your work on the map.

1. **The purpose of my map is** ______________________

____

2. **I got my information from** ______________________

____

Check the word you think best describes your work on this map.

3. **I found and used enough information.**
   ○ Yes ○ No ○ Partly
4. **I used appropriate symbols and included a key and a compass rose.**
   ○ Yes ○ No ○ Partly
5. **I tried hard to place things accurately.**
   ○ Yes ○ No ○ Partly
6. **I think my map achieves its purpose.**
   ○ Yes ○ No ○ Partly
7. **I am satisfied with the result.**
   ○ Yes ○ No ○ Partly

   Explanation ______________________

Complete these statements to evaluate your work on the map.

8. **What I learned from making this map is** ______________________

____

9. **What I like most about my map is** ______________________

____

10. **What could make my map better is** ______________________

____

Student ______________________ Date ______________

Evaluation

Informative Writing

Assignment ______________________

Objective ______________________

Rate each statement about the informative writing according to this scale:

4 = Excellent 3 = Very Good 2 = Acceptable 1 = Needs Improvement

	Statement	Rating (circle one)			
1.	**Your writing fits the purpose and the audience.**	**4**	**3**	**2**	**1**
2.	**You stated your main idea clearly.**	**4**	**3**	**2**	**1**
3.	**All your information fits the main idea.**	**4**	**3**	**2**	**1**
4.	**You gathered and presented enough information to explain the idea.**	**4**	**3**	**2**	**1**
5.	**You arranged your details in a way that makes sense and kept to your main point.**	**4**	**3**	**2**	**1**
6.	**Any visual aids are clear and helpful.**	**4**	**3**	**2**	**1**
7.	**You show an understanding of the history, geography, economics, or culture involved.**	**4**	**3**	**2**	**1**
8.	**You helped the reader by using correct spelling, grammar, punctuation, and capitalization.**	**4**	**3**	**2**	**1**

Overall Evaluation

9. The best part of your work is ______________________

____

10. The part that could be improved is ______________________

____

Name ______________________________ Date ________________

Self-Assessment

Informative Writing

Complete these sentences about your writing assignment.

1. **The assignment was** ______________________________

2. **My topic was** ______________________________

3. **My main idea was** ______________________________

Check the word you think best describes your work on this assignment.

4. **I knew my topic well enough to explain it to others.**
   ○ Yes ○ No ○ Partly

5. **I gathered all the facts I needed.**
   ○ Yes ○ No ○ Partly

6. **I kept my audience in mind and wrote so they could understand.**
   ○ Yes ○ No ○ Partly

7. **I carefully considered readers' suggestions.**
   ○ Yes ○ No ○ Partly

8. **I checked grammar, capitalization, punctuation, and spelling.**
   ○ Yes ○ No ○ Partly

Complete these sentences about your work on this assignment.

9. **The hardest part was** ______________________________
   ____

10. **What I like best about my work is** ______________________________
    ____

11. **What I like least is** ______________________________
    ____

12. **By writing on this topic, I learned** ______________________________
    ____

Student ______________________ Date ______________

Evaluation

Narrative Writing

Assignment ______________________

Objective ______________________

Rate each statement about the piece of writing according to this scale:

4 = Excellent **3 = Very Good** **2 = Acceptable** **1 = Needs Improvement**

		Rating (circle one)			
1.	**Your beginning grabbed my attention.**	**4**	**3**	**2**	**1**
2.	**You told events in order, as they happened.**	**4**	**3**	**2**	**1**
3.	**You connected events so that it was easy to follow the action.**	**4**	**3**	**2**	**1**
4.	**You used appropriate details and dialogue to bring the narrative to life.**	**4**	**3**	**2**	**1**
5.	**Your ending gave a fitting resolution.**	**4**	**3**	**2**	**1**
6.	**You showed an understanding of the people, places, cultures, and events you were writing about.**	**4**	**3**	**2**	**1**
7.	**You helped the reader by using correct spelling, grammar, punctuation, and capitalization.**	**4**	**3**	**2**	**1**

Overall Evaluation

8. I liked best the way you ______________________

____

____

9. You need to pay more attention to ______________________

____

____

Name ______________________ Date ______________

Self-Assessment

Narrative Writing

Complete these sentences about your writing assignment.

1. The assignment was ______________________

2. I wrote about ______________________

3. My title was ______________________

Check the word you think best describes your work on this assignment.

4. I gathered enough information about people, places, and events involved.

○ Yes ○ No ○ Partly

5. I presented the events in the order in which they happened.

○ Yes ○ No ○ Partly

6. I used suitable details and dialogue to make the narrative interesting and authentic.

○ Yes ○ No ○ Partly

7. I carefully considered readers' suggestions.

○ Yes ○ No ○ Partly

8. I checked grammar, punctuation, capitalization, and spelling.

○ Yes ○ No ○ Partly

Complete each sentence about your work on this assignment.

9. I especially like the way I ______________________

____

10. What I like least about my work is ______________________

____

11. Next time I think I will ______________________

____

12. By writing this narrative, I learned ______________________

____

Student ______________________ Date ______________

Evaluation

Descriptive Writing

Assignment ______________________

Objective ______________________

Rate each statement about the descriptive writing according to this scale:

4 = Excellent 3 = Very Good 2 = Acceptable 1 = Needs Improvement

		Rating (circle one)			
1.	**You stated your main idea clearly.**	**4**	**3**	**2**	**1**
2.	**All your details support the main idea.**	**4**	**3**	**2**	**1**
3.	**You arranged your details in a way that makes sense and kept to that organization.**	**4**	**3**	**2**	**1**
4.	**You used specific details that helped me picture the subject in my mind.**	**4**	**3**	**2**	**1**
5.	**You described the time, place, and people accurately.**	**4**	**3**	**2**	**1**
6.	**You showed an understanding of the history, geography, economics, or culture involved.**	**4**	**3**	**2**	**1**
7.	**You helped the reader by using correct spelling, grammar, punctuation, and capitalization.**	**4**	**3**	**2**	**1**

Overall Evaluation

8. The best part of your work is ______________________

____

____

9. The part that could be improved is ______________________

____

____

Name ______________________ Date ______________

Self-Assessment

Descriptive Writing

Complete these sentences about your writing assignment.

1. The assignment was ______________________
2. I wrote about ______________________
3. My title is ______________________

Check the word you think best describes your work on this assignment.

4. I gathered enough information about people, places, and events.
   ○ Yes ○ No ○ Partly
5. I described one feature at a time and arranged my details in a way that made sense.
   ○ Yes ○ No ○ Partly
6. I pictured my subject as I wrote and tried to describe it exactly.
   ○ Yes ○ No ○ Partly
7. I carefully considered readers' suggestions.
   ○ Yes ○ No ○ Partly
8. I checked grammar, capitalization, punctuation, and spelling.
   ○ Yes ○ No ○ Partly

Complete each sentence about your work on this assignment.

9. I especially like the way I ______________________
   ____
10. What I like least is ______________________
    ____
11. Next time I think I will ______________________
    ____
12. By writing this description, I learned ______________________
    ____

Student ______________________ Date ______________

Evaluation

Expressive Writing

Assignment ______________________

Objective ______________________

Rate each statement about the expressive writing according to this scale:

4 = Excellent 3 = Very Good 2 = Acceptable 1 = Needs Improvement

		Rating (circle one)			
1.	**You seemed to understand the assignment.**	**4**	**3**	**2**	**1**
2.	**Your details and language fit your audience.**	**4**	**3**	**2**	**1**
3.	**You used details that made your thoughts and feelings clear.**	**4**	**3**	**2**	**1**
4.	**You arranged your details in a way that makes sense and kept to that organization.**	**4**	**3**	**2**	**1**
5.	**You show an understanding of the people, places, and events involved.**	**4**	**3**	**2**	**1**
6.	**You expressed yourself in a creative and interesting way.**	**4**	**3**	**2**	**1**
7.	**You helped the reader by correcting spelling, grammar, punctuation, and capitalization.**	**4**	**3**	**2**	**1**

Overall Evaluation

8. The best part of your work is ______________________

____

9. The part that could be improved is ______________________

____

Name ______________________ Date ______________

Self-Assessment

Expressive Writing

Complete these sentences about your writing assignment.

1. **The assignment was** ______________________
2. **I wrote about** ______________________
3. **My title is** ______________________

Check the word you think best describes your work on this assignment.

4. **I knew exactly what I wanted to express.**
   ○ Yes ○ No ○ Partly
5. **I gathered information that helped me express it.**
   ○ Yes ○ No ○ Partly
6. **I succeeded in expressing my feelings.**
   ○ Yes ○ No ○ Partly
7. **I carefully considered readers' suggestions.**
   ○ Yes ○ No ○ Partly
8. **I checked grammar, punctuation, capitalization, and spelling.**
   ○ Yes ○ No ○ Partly

Complete each sentence about your work on this piece of writing.

9. **I especially like the way I** ______________________
10. **What I like least about my work is** ______________________
11. **Next time I think I will** ______________________
12. **By writing this piece, I learned** ______________________

Student ______________________ Date ______________

Evaluation

Research Reports

Assignment ______________________

Objective ______________________

Rate each statement about the research report according to this scale:

4 = Excellent **3 = Very Good** **2 = Acceptable** **1 = Needs Improvement**

	Rating (circle one)			
1. The introduction states the topic and main idea.	4	3	2	1
2. Ideas and details are organized in a way that makes sense.	4	3	2	1
3. You included enough information to make your points clear and convincing.	4	3	2	1
4. The conclusion summarizes the main points.	4	3	2	1
5. The list of sources seems complete and correct.	4	3	2	1
6. You show an understanding of the history, economics, geography, and culture involved.	4	3	2	1
7. You distinguish fact from opinion and your own opinions from the opinions of others.	4	3	2	1
8. You helped the reader by correcting grammar, punctuation, capitalization, and spelling.	4	3	2	1

Overall Evaluation

9. The best part of your work is ______________________

____

10. The part that could be improved is ______________________

____

Name ______________________ Date ______________

Self-Assessment

Research Reports

1. **The assignment was** ______________________
2. **My title is** ______________________
3. **My main idea is** ______________________

Check the word you think best describes your work on this report.

4. **I understood my topic well enough to explain it.**
   ○ Yes ○ No ○ Partly
5. **I made the topic clear to my audience.**
   ○ Yes ○ No ○ Partly
6. **I used my own words, except for exact quotations.**
   ○ Yes ○ No ○ Partly
7. **I gave serious attention to suggestions from readers.**
   ○ Yes ○ No ○ Partly
8. **I checked grammar, punctuation, capitalization, and spelling.**
   ○ Yes ○ No ○ Partly

Complete each sentence to describe your work on this report.

9. **I especially like the way I** ______________________
   ____
10. **What I like least about my work is** ______________________
    ____
11. **Next time I think I will** ______________________
    ____
12. **By writing this piece, I learned** ______________________
    ____

Answer Key

Unit 1

Chapter 1 Test pg. 1

1. C [Obj. 1.1]
2. B [Obj. 1.1]
3. C [Obj. 1.2]
4. B [Obj. 1.2]
5. A [Obj. 2.1]
6. C [Obj. 2.1]
7. B [Obj. 2.2]
8. A [Obj. 2.2]
9. B [Obj. 3.1]
10. C [Obj. 3.1]
11. B [Obj. 3.2]
12. D [Obj. 3.2]
13. basin
14. immigrant
15. culture
16. mineral
17. reservoir
18. landform
19. irrigation
20. An X should appear in the Southwest or in California.
21. Students should put an X on a state in the Midwest.
22. Samples: plateau—high, flat land that rises above the nearby land on at least one side; mountains—tall peaks; plains—flat land with some rolling hills. [Obj. 1.1]
23. Rich natural resources,such as energy resources, minerals, and farmland, have helped make the United States a rich country. [Obj. 1.2]
24. Yes, because there are several types of regions, such as physical regions, cultural regions, and economic regions. [Obj. 2.1]
25. Answers should explain how a particular holiday is a reflection of the culture—either general American culture or the culture of a specific group. [Obj. 2.2]
26. Answer should cover some local feature such as steep roofs, porches, building material, etc. that is adapted to local climate. [Obj. 3.1]
27. Good effects—water for irrigation, recreation areas, and flood control. Bad—environmental damage to the Colorado River. [Obj. 3.2]
28. California
29. The area went from being very sparsely populated to being much more densely populated.
30. Accept reasonable responses such as better climate, ports, immigration, Gold Rush, etc.

Chapter 2 Test pg. 6

1. D [Obj. 1-1]
2. B [Obj. 1-2]
3. C [Obj. 2-1]
4. C [Obj. 2-2]
5. A [Obj. 3-1]
6. D [Obj. 3-2]
7. C [Obj. 4-1]
8. B [Obj. 4-2]
9. B [Obj. 4-1]
10. D [Obj. 1-2]
11. glacier
12. confederacy
13. surplus
14. drought
15. pueblo
16. C
17. B
18. Sample: Hunters followed game animals across the land bridge. [Obj. 1-1]
19. Sample: People needed different weapons such as bows and arrows to hunt small game. They need tools to grind wild grain and seeds. [Obj. 1-2]
20. People learned new skills. While some people remained farmers, others became warriors or priests. [Obj. 2-1]
21. The dry climate forced the Anasazi to irrigate crops. [Obj. 1-2]
22. Wood and bark were commonly used. Northern homes had thick sides, while houses in the South were more open. Many groups had long houses with many families. [Obj. 3-1]
23. The central plazas were the center of religious ceremonies. Buildings located around the plaza were also important for council meetings and storage. [Obj. 3-2]
24. Sample: the giving of gifts during potlatches; the abundance of natural resources. [Obj. 4-1]
25. Sample: Both good and evil lay within each person; after death, that evil became a dangerous ghost. [Obj. 4-2]
26. In 100 B.C.
27. Around A.D. 900
28. In the twelfth century A.D.
29. About 1250 years

Unit 1 Open-ended Response pg. 11

The answer should clearly relate land form and resources to the way of life of a particular group. Some possible examples include irrigation in the Southwest, use of forest resources by Native Americans in the woodlands, present-day use of national parks, and so on.

Unit 2

Chapter 3 Test pg. 16

1. C [Obj. 1-1]
2. A [Obj. 1-1]
3. C [Obj. 1-1]
4. B [Obj. 1-2]
5. D [Obj. 1-2]
6. A [Obj. 2-1]
7. C [Obj. 2-1]
8. D [Obj. 2-2]
9. C [Obj. 2-2]
10. emperor
11. saga
12. merchant
13. pilgrimage
14. Islam
15. Leif Ericson
16. salt
17. They concluded that Vikings must have had a settlement in that area. [Obj. 1-1]
18. When Mansa Mansu returned to Timbuktu, he brought Arab scholars with him. [Obj. 1-2]
19. Samples: The Chinese had inventions such as paper money and gunpowder. They had an empire with good roads, good communication, and fine palaces. [Obj. 2-1]
20. The Greek and Roman cultures. [Obj. 2-2]
21. The group arrived at the North Pole on Earth Day and shared accounts of its adventures with students through the Internet.
22. It's a problem that people need to become aware of.
23. Accept any topic related to pollution. Sample media: magazines and newspapers

Chapter 4 Test pg. 21

1. D [Obj. 1.1]
2. B [Obj. 1.2]
3. D [Obj. 2.1]
4. A [Obj. 2.2]
5. B [Obj. 3.1]
6. A [Obj. 3.2]
7. C [Obj. 4.1]
8. B [Obj. 4.2]
9. D [Obj. 4.1]
10. A [Obj. 4.2]
11. settlement
12. rebel
13. epidemic
14. navigation
15. slavery
16. C
17. B
18. Students can answer yes or no. Samples: No, because the compass let sailors navigate out of sight of land because it indicates where north is. Yes, because the Portuguese could have used the astrolabe and the cross-staff to reach Asia. [Obj. 1.1]
19. He probably took about the same route each time. [Obj. 1.2]
20. The only evidence was an old legend about Africa. The lure of gold probably kept explorers looking for them.
21. Africans were enslaved by the Spanish to work on Caribbean sugar plantations. Sugar was a crop brought from Europe as part of the Columbian exchange. [Obj. 3.1]
22. Sample: Europeans wanted to set up farms, so they brought livestock animals. In the Americas, people relied on wild animals, not domestic ones, for meat. [Obj. 3.2]
23. The population went down because many Native Americans died in war, from being enslaved, or from diseases brought by the Europeans. [Obj. 3.2]
24. To invade and conquer England. [Obj. 4.1]
25. Each wanted a trading advantage over the other countries. [Obj. 4.2]
26. 74° W longitude
27. 1°
28. 41° (or 40° 30') N 74° W
29. About 30 miles. Each minute of latitude is about 1 mile.

Chapter 5 Test pg. 26

1. D [Obj. 1.1]
2. C [Obj. 1.2]
3. C [Obj. 2.1]
4. A [Obj. 2.2]
5. D [Obj. 3.1]
6. C [Obj. 3.2]
7. B [Obj. 4.1]
8. C [Obj. 4.2]
9. B [Obj. 1.2; 4.1]
10. D [Obj. 1.1; 3.1; 4.1]
11. charter
12. patroon
13. colony
14. viceroy
15. invest
16. D
17. C
18. Native Americans, because the Spanish forced them to. [Obj. 1.1]
19. Many of them wanted to practice their own religion. [Obj. 1.2]
20. It shows daily life, including the houses the Algonquin lived in and the crops they grew. [Obj. 2.1]
21. Sample: The colony would not have found a crop to make the colonists rich. The colony might have failed. The colonists would not have relied on indentured servants and enslaved Africans to grow the tobacco. [Obj. 2.2]
22. It would have rules to govern the school community. [Obj. 3.1]
23. Because he planned carefully for the settlement, had a vision of its purpose, and governed it for many years. [Obj. 3.2]
24. Both were Catholic missionaries whose goal was to convert Native Americans to Christianity. Both set up missions as the basis of settlement. [Obj. 4.1]
25. The Dutch wanted the colony to grow, so they welcomed people of different nations. [Obj. 4.2]
26. Sentence 1—secondary, because it summarizes events and does not contain personal observation. Sentence 2—primary, because it uses words like our and we
27. Fact: settlers ate dogs, cats, rats, snakes, toadstools, and horsehides. It is a vivid way of showing the settlers' problems.

Unit 2 Open-ended Response pg. 31

The answer should reflect a knowledge of a specific explorer and his achievements. Qualities chosen can be positive ones like courage or negative ones such as greed, but should be linked to specific actions.

Unit 3

Chapter 6 Test pg. 36

1. D [Obj. 1.1]
2. A [Obj. 1.1]
3. C [Obj. 1.2]
4. B [Obj. 1.2]
5. A [Obj. 2.1]
6. B [Obj. 2.1]
7. A [Obj. 2.2]
8. B [Obj. 2.2]
9. B [Obj. 3.1]
10. D [Obj. 3.1]
11. C [Obj. 3.2]
12. B [Obj. 3.2]
13. wampum
14. self-sufficient
15. triangular trade
16. meetinghouse
17. imports
18. Students should mark Boston's location.
19. Students should mark Rhode Island.
20. Because glaciers had removed the good soil. [Obj. 1.1]
21. The size depended on the size of the family and the family's importance in the community. Students who believe the system was fair may point to the way it met the needs of the family and the community. Students who believe it was unfair may suggest that each family should have received the same size plot. [Obj. 1.2]
22. By introducing religious beliefs that differed from those of the original Puritans. [Obj. 2.1]
23. It was fought between Native Americans and colonial settlers because of the spreading settlements. The Puritans won the war and gained control of the land. [Obj. 2.2]
24. Children then spent most of their time doing chores. Families would not have survived without the children's work. [Obj. 3.1]
25. Boston was a seaport. It was a center of fishing and trade. [Obj. 3.2]
26. the green.
27. It is much larger today.
28. It is the same in some places but some roads are different today and there are more streets now.

Chapter 7 Test pg. 41

1. C [Obj. 1.1]
2. A [Obj. 1.1]
3. D [Obj. 2.1]
4. B [Obj. 2.1]
5. D [Obj. 2.2]
6. C [Obj. 2.2]
7. C [Obj. 3.1]
8. B [Obj. 3.1]
9. C [Obj. 3.2]
10. D [Obj. 3.2]
11. subsistence
12. yeoman
13. backcountry
14. Piedmont
15. apprentice
16. New York
17. Philadelphia
18. Pennsylvania-New Jersey border
19. Students should draw a line between the mountains and the coast.
20. Waterfalls kept boats from going farther up the rivers. But the waterfalls were a source of power for sawmills and gristmills. [Obj. 1.1]
21. Both are named for their proprietors—William Penn and the Duke of York. [Obj. 2.1]
22. Germans, Scots-Irish, and settlers from other colonies were attracted by rich farmland and religious toleration. [Obj. 2.2]
23. It was ground into flour, sent down the river by barge, and sold to American towns or exported to Britain and the Caribbean. [Obj. 3.1]
24. Accept any two: The city was in an excellent location to be a trading center. It had no walls because Penn expected the colonists and Native Americans to live in peace. The grid pattern shows that the location of streets was planned. [Obj. 3.2]
25. an afternoon hailstorm
26. hail or hailstorm
27. "so that" or "so"
28. Students should fill in hailstorm as the cause and two effects, such as the white ground and broken glass.

Chapter 8 Test pg. 46

1. A [Obj. 1.1]
2. B [Obj. 1.1]
3. C [Obj. 1.2]
4. A [Obj. 1.2]
5. C [Obj. 2.2]
6. D [Obj. 2.2]
7. B [Obj. 3.1]
8. B [Obj. 3.1]
9. D [Obj. 3.2]
10. C [Obj. 3.2]
11. debtor
12. tidewater
13. export
14. representative
15. profit
16. corn
17. Maryland
18. Students should defend their answers with reasons that reflect an understanding of the South's agriculture. Sample: indigo, because it sells for a high price. [Obj. 1.1]
19. Rich planters, because the planters controlled the House of Burgesses. [Obj. 2.1]
20. South Carolina had rich soil, navigable rivers, and wide harbors. North Carolina was hilly, with poor soil and few rivers. [Obj. 2.2]
21. They were the center of social life, acting as meetinghouses, taverns, and post offices. [Obj. 3.1]
22. Plantations mostly grew cash crops for export. Plantations had the richest land; much of the work was done by enslaved Africans. [Obj. 3.2]
23. The arrow to the West Indies—most people went there.
24. People moved from England to the Americas.
25. Twice as many people went to the Chesapeake.

Unit 3 Open-ended Response pg. 51

The student's answer should reflect a knowledge of a specific colony and its relative advantages. Any of the colonies may be used as an answer, but the reasons should be specific and stated clearly.

Unit 4

Chapter 9 Test pg. 56

1. C [Obj. 1.1]
2. A [Obj. 1.1]
3. A [Obj. 1.2]
4. B [[Obj. 1.2]
5. A [Obj. 2.1]
6. D [Obj. 2.1
7. B [Obj. 2.2]
8. C [Obj. 2.2]
9. congress
10. duty
11. boycott
12. ally
13. proclamation
14. Britain
15. imported goods like tea and paint
16. To side with the British against the French. [Obj. 1.1]
17. The Proclamation line of 1763. The British government said that the land to the west of the line was owned by Native Americans and colonists were forbidden to settle there. [Obj. 1.2]
18. Almost everything printed on paper [Obj. 2.1]
19. Since the boycott made British merchants lose money, the merchants asked Parliament to repeal the Townshend Acts. [Obj. 2.2]
20. Yes. Fortifications were located between Montcalm's headquarters and the water.
21. He went by land, traveling southwest.
22. Probably a bad idea because the route was well-fortified.

Chapter 10 Test pg. 61

1. D [Obj. 1.1]
2. A [Obj. 1.1]
3. C [Obj. 1.2]
4. B [Obj. 1.2]
5. C [Obj. 2.1]
6. C [Obj. 2.1]
7. B [Obj. 2.2]
8. D [Obj. 2.2]
9. C [Obj. 3.1]
10. A [Obj. 3.1]
11. B [Obj. 3.2]
12. D [Obj. 3.2]
13. propaganda
14. petition
15. militia
16. peninsula
17. delegate
18. 1776
19. Thomas Jefferson
20. They were outraged and used the incident as propaganda. [Obj. 1.1]
21. Parliament passed the acts to punish the colonists for the Boston Tea Party. [Obj. 1.2]
22. Accept answers such as the large presence of British troops, the effects of the Intolerable Acts, the presence of many colonial leaders in Boston, the training of the Minutemen, and the tension in the colony. [Obj. 2.1]
23. Since the colonists fought so well, they would feel encouraged about the possibility of winning a war against the British Army. [Obj. 2.2]
24. Common Sense spoke for many people in the colonies who sought their liberty in breaking away from British rule. [Obj. 3.1]
25. the rights to life, liberty, and the pursuit of happiness [Obj. 3.2]
26. before
27. king or majesty
28. They describe themselves as "faithful subjects," and they probably hoped that this would gain the favor of the British government.

Chapter 11 Test pg 66

1. D [Obj. 1.1]
2. A [Obj. 1.1]
3. C [Obj. 1.2]
4. B [Obj. 1.2]
5. B [Obj. 2.1]
6. C [Obj. 2.1]
7. C [Obj. 2.2]
8. A [Obj. 2.2]
9. B [Obj. 3.1]
10. D [Obj. 3.1]
11. C [Obj. 3.2]
12. A [Obj. 3.2]
13. strategy
14. diplomat
15. surrender
16. revolution
17. negotiate
18. Valley Forge
19. Marquis de Lafayette
20. Sample: Strength—fighting on familiar ground; Weakness—poor training. [Obj. 1.1]
21. The British might have captured Washington and his troops. The British might then have won the war. [Obj. 1.2]
22. The victory at Saratoga, because it made France believe in the possibility of a Patriot victory. [Obj. 2.1]
23. Marion kept on attacking in small hit-and-run raids. [Obj. 2.2]
24. It established the new nation's borders: Canada, the Mississippi, and Spanish Florida. [Obj. 3.1]
25. They fled to Canada, Britain, or the British West Indies. Some African American Loyalists returned to Africa. [Obj. 3.2]
26. Students should mark a spot near Bear Tavern.
27. Students should mark Trenton.
28. Students should mark the River Road.

Unit 4 Open-ended Response pg. 71

The student's answer should reflect a knowledge of the events of the American Revolution and an understanding of a Patriot's point of view.

Unit 5

Chapter 12 Test pg. 76

1. B [Obj. 1.1]
2. C [Obj. 1.2]
3. A [Obj. 2.1]
4. C [Obj. 2.2]
5. A [Obj. 3.1]
6. B [Obj. 3.2]
7. A [Obj. 4.1]
8. B [Obj. 4.2]
9. D [Obj. 3.1]
10. D [Obj. 2.2]
11. political party
12. compromise
13. constitution
14. legislative branch
15. democracy
16. James Madison
17. Bill of Rights
18. A weak national government could not hurt them the way the strong British Parliament had. People felt that power should belong to the states. [Obj. 1.1]
19. It made people believe that the government was too weak and that the Articles of Confederation needed to be changed. [Obj. 1.2]
20. No. Groups not represented included women, African Americans, and Native Americans. [Obj. 2.1]
21. In the Senate, each state has the same number of votes. In the House of Representatives, each state is represented according to the size of its population. [Obj. 2.2]
22. Sample: the power to raise taxes. [Obj. 3.1]
23. Sample: the outlawing of slavery. [Obj. 3.2]
24. He was a model for other presidents to follow. He set precedents such as having a cabinet. [Obj. 4.1]
25. Hamilton thought that a strong national government was necessary to keep order. Jefferson thought that a national government that was too strong could threaten people's freedom. [Obj. 4.2]
26. by the city council
27. by the voters in an election
28. the city manager

Chapter 13 Test pg. 81

1. D [Obj. 1.1]
2. B [Obj. 1.1]
3. D [Obj. 1.2]
4. C [Obj. 1.2]
5. D [Obj. 2.1]
6. A [Obj. 2.1]
7. A [Obj. 2.2]
8. C [Obj. 2.2]
9. D [Obj. 3.1]
10. C [Obj. 3.1]
11. C [Obj. 3.2]
12. B [Obj. 3.2]
13. Correct section of the map should be shaded.
14. circles around the beginning (Mississippi) and end (Pacific) of the northern of the two routes
15. He opened the way west for many Americans. He made a trail across the Appalachians called the "Wilderness Trail. [Obj. 1.1]
16. to find a water route across the continent and to learn more about the geography of the West [Obj. 1.2]
17. No. The Battle of Tippecanoe destroyed his dream of a Native American union to drive away the white man. [Obj. 2.1]
18. They increased because Americans had been successful against the British. [Obj. 2.2]
19. to inspire Americans and add to Washington's glory [Obj. 3.1]
20. Sample: types of writing implements, supplies, and equipment; subjects taught; ages and types of people in class. [Obj. 3.2]
21. expedition
22. hero
23. impressment
24. frontier
25. symbol
26. James Daugherty
27. Sample: Lewis had $2500 to spend to buy needed supplies for the expedition.
28. "bronze medals with Jefferson's head on one side and hands clasped in peace on the other"

Unit 5 Open-ended Response pg. 86

The answer should reflect a knowledge of the Constitution and its provisions. Specific sections supporting Washington's point might be the election of representatives, the power of amendment, and so on. Students might also point out that government rests on the consent of the governed. or that the people, through the state legislatures, voted on the Constitution itself.

Unit 6

Chapter 14 Test pg. 91

1. B [Obj. 1.1]
2. A [Obj. 1.2]
3. B [Obj. 2.1]
4. C [Obj. 2.2]
5. C [Obj. 3.1]
6. A [Obj. 3.2]
7. D [Obj. 4.1]
8. D [Obj. 4.2]
9. B [Obj. 1.1]
10. A [Obj. 3.2]
11. Industrial Revolution
12. suffrage
13. tenement
14. candidate
15. abolitionist
16. Eli Whitney
17. equality for women
18. The new states gave suffrage to all white men. In the older states, only men who owned property could vote. [Obj. 1.1]
19. The journey of the Cherokee when they were forced out of their homeland and moved to territory west of the Mississippi [Obj. 1.2]
20. It made the economy of the western states grow because farmers in the west could send their products back east. [Obj. 2.1]
21. Sample: Mill work offered independence and a chance to earn money. But the mill girls worked long, hard days in noisy factories. [Obj. 2.2]
22. Sample: They tried to escape to freedom. They took part in rebellions. [Obj. 3.1]
23. The Irish came because the potato crop failed. Most settled in Northern cities. The Germans came to escape economic and political trouble. Most settled in the Midwest. [Obj. 3.2]
24. When several women were treated badly at the World Anti-Slavery Convention, they worked together to start a movement for women's rights. [Obj. 4.1]
25. Mann worked to improve schools. His work led to a law requiring students to go to school. [Obj. 4.2]
26. The graph shows where immigrants came from in 1854. Each section shows how many immigrants came from each country or geographic area.
27. Immigration increased sharply from the mid-1840s to mid 1850s.
28. line

Chapter 15 Test pg. 96

1. B [Obj. 1.1]
2. A [Obj. 1.1]
3. D [Obj. 1.2]
4. D [Obj. 1.2]
5. C [Obj. 2.1]
6. A [Obj. 2.1]
7. C [Obj. 2.2]
8. D [Obj. 2.2]
9. B [Obj. 3.1]
10. A [Obj. 3.1]
11. C [Obj. 3.2]
12. B [Obj. 3.2]
13. Alamo
14. Santa Fe Trail
15. Many more Anglo-Americans came than Mexico planned on. The Mexicans in Texas were outnumbered by Anglo-Americans. Soon the Anglo-Americans wanted independence. [Obj. 1.1]
16. The idea stated that the United States should expand across the continent; it made Americans enthusiastic about annexing Texas and going to war with Mexico. [Obj. 1.2]
17. Sample: long, difficult trip; bad weather; dangers such as stampedes, prairie fires, and avalanches. [Obj. 2.1]
18. The Rocky Mountains were a huge geographic obstacle. Pioneers needed trails so they could find passes in the mountains. [Obj. 2.2]
19. Marshall and Sutter hoped to make money by keeping the gold. Brannan wanted to make money by having many people come West to look for gold. Then they would buy things at his store. [Obj. 3.1]
20. These towns were mining towns that sprang up quickly. Most turned into ghost towns when the gold and silver ran out. [Obj. 3.2]
21. pass
22. Continental Divide
23. Manifest Destiny
24. annexation
25. dispute
26. 12,117 feet
27. It stays about the same elevation for a long way.
28. The contour lines are closer together.

Unit 6 Open-ended Response pg. 101

The answer should reflect a knowledge of the time period and the experiences of settlers. Students might write about the length of the journey, the dangers that settlers faced, the experience of traveling in a cramped wagon, and the excitement of anticipating a new life and a new home.

Unit 7

Chapter 16 Test pg. 106

1. A [Obj. 1.1]
2. A [Obj. 1.2]
3. C [Obj. 2.1]
4. B [Obj. 2.2]
5. C [Obj. 3.1]
6. C [Obj. 3.2]
7. D [Obj. 4.1]
8. C [Obj. 4.2]
9. D [Obj. 1.1]
10. C [Obj. 2.1]
11. contraband
12. mobilize
13. inflation
14. draft
15. secede
16. Uncle Tom's Cabin
17. Robert E. Lee
18. The South had more power in the Senate than in the House of Representatives. Representation in the Senate was by state, so the Southern and Northern states had an equal number of votes. But representation in the House was by population, and the North had more people than the South. [Obj. 1.1]
19. In the Dred Scott decision, the Supreme Court ruled that Congress could not prevent slave owners from bringing enslaved people into new territory. The decision erased the Missouri Compromise and made northerners angry. [Obj. 1.2]
20. Sample: More people, better industry and transportation, more money to buy supplies. Abraham Lincoln was a strong, determined leader. [Obj. 2.1]
21. The North wanted to prevent the South from shipping its products or buying military supplies. [Obj. 2.2]
22. Two of these: Freed African Americans could help the North fight. Ending slavery would keep England from helping the South. Public opinion in the North supported emancipation. [Obj. 3.1]
23. At first, African American soldiers were paid less than whites. In 1864, Congress corrected this. [Obj. 3.2]
24. farmers, factory workers, teachers, saleswomen, government clerks. [Obj. 4.1]
25. Rich men could pay money and not have to serve. Rich slaveowners in the South didn't have to fight. Some students may think this was unfair because poor men had to fight in the place of rich men; others may think it was fair because the rich made other contributions to the war. [Obj. 4.2]
26. Sample: his cap and his rifle
27. Students may suggest that he looks tired or depressed. Accept all reasonable responses.
28. The uniform and other details would show more clearly.

Chapter 17 Test pg. 111

1. B [Obj. 1.1]
2. D [Obj. 1.1]
3. A [Obj. 1.2]
4. A [Obj. 1.2]
5. D [Obj. 2.1]
6. D [Obj. 2.1]
7. A [Obj. 2.2]
8. C [Obj. 2.2]
9. D [Obj. 3.1]
10. A [Obj. 3.1]
11. B [Obj. 3.2]
12. C [Obj. 3.2]
13. impeach
14. segregation
15. credit
16. desertion
17. assassinate
18. the Gettysburg Address
19. at Appomattox Courthouse
20. It made them suffer. They didn't have enough food. Crops and houses were destroyed. They lost their jobs. [Obj. 1.1]
21. Both sides were part of the same country. The Union soldiers needed to remember that the Southerners were Americans. Grant wanted to create a spirit of forgiveness. [Obj. 1.2]
22. Sample: They knew that being able to read and write would help them adjust to freedom, find jobs, and help their children to a better life. [Obj. 2.1]
23. Because of the Black Codes, African Americans were prevented from voting, traveling, or doing certain kinds of work. Sharecropping kept African Americans dependent on landowners. [Obj. 2.2]
24. Radical Republicans believed that the national government should do everything necessary to protect the rights of African Americans. President Andrew Johnson believed that the states could decide how to govern their citizens, including African Americans. [Obj. 3.1]
25. It prevented most African Americans from voting.
26. Gettysburg Address or Gettysburg
27. print it out
28. Accept reasonable questions.

Unit 7 Open-ended Response pg. 116

The answer should reflect a knowledge of differences between the North and the South. Students might point out, for example, that the North had more industry than the South. Material in the organizer should contain parallel information for the North and the South; the organizer should be appropriately labeled.

Unit 8

Chapter 18 Test pg. 121

1. C [Obj. 1.1]
2. A [Obj. 1.1]
3. D [Obj. 1.2]
4. B [Obj. 1.2]
5. C [Obj. 2.1]
6. A [Obj. 2.1]
7. D [Obj. 2.2]
8. C [Obj. 2.2]
9. D [Obj. 3.1]
10. C [Obj. 3.1]
11. A [Obj. 3.2]
12. B [Obj. 3.2]
13. homestead
14. reservation
15. telegraph
16. pony express
17. dry farming
18. Samuel Morse
19. Geronimo
20. The telegraph was better because it was much faster. [Obj. 1.1]
21. The Union Pacific and Central Pacific tracks met to form the transcontinental railroad. [Obj. 1.2]
22. Because cattle ranchers began to make greater profits by shipping their cattle to the East. [Obj. 2.1]
23. so the land where Native Americans once lived could go to settlers [Obj. 2.2]
24. for pumping water from the ground [Obj. 3.1]
25. Wheat prices dropped, and the farmers lost money. The Grange enabled them to band together to save money on purchases. [Obj. 3.2]
26. where Native Americans live in the United States
27. changes in the Native American population from 1500 to 1980
28. The graph shows change over time, but the map shows only the present. The map shows the locations where Native Americans live today, but the graph has no information about location.

Chapter 19 Test pg. 126

1. A [Obj. 1.1]
2. B [Obj. 1.2]
3. A [Obj. 2.1]
4. B [Obj. 2.2]
5. C [Obj. 3.1]
6. D [Obj. 3.2]
7. B [Obj. 4.1]
8. D [Obj. 4.2]
9. C [Obj. 3.2]
10. A [Obj. 2.1]
11. strike
12. entrepreneur
13. monopoly
14. yellow journalism
15. mechanization
16. the Statue of Liberty
17. Alexander Graham Bell
18. The Bessemer process was a way of making steel. Steel railroad tracks were stronger than iron tracks. Bigger and faster trains could be built to run on the steel tracks. [Obj. 1.1]
19. Sample: A person would need to work hard, be intelligent, be willing to take a risk, and be aware of which businesses were likely to grow and succeed. [Obj. 1.2]
20. Children learned English in school. They also learned American customs and culture. [Obj. 2.1]
21. Immigrants could adjust to America while living with people who shared their language and culture. [Obj. 2.2]
22. Yes. There was no law against children working and no law saying that children had to go to school. Families needed the income. [Obj. 3.1]
23. A business can usually be run without one worker but not without all the workers. [Obj. 3.2]
24. The planters called on the United States for help. The U.S. Marines helped overthrow the queen. [Obj. 4.1]
25. As a result of its victory, the United States acquired overseas territories. [Obj. 4.2]
26. Threatening. The entrance has a drawbridge and metal gate. One guard bars the way of the immigrant.
27. That unlike immigrants from many other countries, Chinese immigrants were not then welcome in the United States.
28. He thinks the immigrants should be allowed to enter.

Unit 8 Open-ended Response pg. 131

The answer should reflect an understanding of the reaction of a specific group to change. Possible examples include the Ghost Dance of the Sioux, the formation of the Grange, the importance of public schools, the role of ethnic neighborhoods and settlement houses, and the rise of labor unions.

Unit 9

Chapter 20 Test pg. 136

1. C [Obj. 1-1]
2. A [Obj. 1-2]
3. D [Obj. 2-1]
4. B [Obj. 2-2]
5. A [Obj. 3-1]
6. D [Obj. 3-2]
7. B [Obj. 4-1]
8. C [Obj. 4-2]
9. B [Obj. 4-1]
10. C [Obj. 3.2]
11. muckrakers
12. Holocaust
13. armistice
14. stock market
15. Axis Powers
16. a founder of the NAACP
17. the League of Nations
18. They thought that government should respond to people's needs and protect the well-being of citizens. [Obj. 1-1]
19. They would have favored laws that improved working conditions and protected workers. [Obj. 1-2]
20. Sample: The war was so terrible that nations would seek new ways to settle disagreements. Countries could discuss problems at the League of Nations rather than going to war. [Obj. 2-1]
21. The American soldiers were fresh and ready to fight on the side of the Allies. This helped the Allies win the war. [Obj. 2-2]
22. Radio came into every home, and sound was added to movies. American culture spread around the world. [Obj. 3-1]
23. He meant that if Americans stopped being afraid and had confidence in themselves and the New Deal programs, the nation would survive the Depression. [Obj. 3-2]

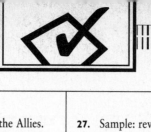

24. The treaty forced Germany to pay money to the Allies. Hitler and his party gained power partly by blaming the Depression on these payments. [Obj. 4-1]
25. Sample: Truman was justified because he wanted to end the war quickly and save American lives, or he was wrong because the bomb was a terrible weapon to use against civilians. Students should support any opinions. [Obj. 4-2]
26. The first graph shows the number of telephones from 1929 to 1945. The second graph shows the number of readers of daily newspapers in the same time period.
27. It is similar. Both lines go down from 1929 to the early 1930s.
28. Telephones and readers both increase. By the late 1930s people had more money. The coming of war probably led more people to read newspapers.

Chapter 21 Test pg. 141

1. D [Obj. 1.1]
2. A [Obj. 1.2]
3. B [Obj. 2.1]
4. C [Obj. 2.2]
5. C [Obj. 3.1]
6. C [Obj. 1.1]
7. A [Obj. 4.1]
8. D [Obj. 4.2]
9. A [Obj. 1.1]
10. B [Obj. 2.2]
11. segregation of schools by race
12. hydrogen bomb
13. The line was like a curtain because it closed off Eastern Europe from Western Europe. [Obj. 1.1]
14. Having more money made people more confident about raising a family. Many people believed in a bright future. They could share it with their children. [Obj. 1.2]
15. Sample: Many African American children could not go to school with white children. African Americans could not use "whites-only" restaurants and hotels. [Obj. 2.1]
16. Sample: They boycotted buses. They went on marches. [Obj. 2.2]
17. It made the war seem very real and people took sides. Some people wanted to send more troops and some people wanted the troops to come home. [Obj. 3.1]
18. Accept two: The United Farm Workers improved farm workers' pay and working conditions. The American Indian Movement fought for Native Americans' civil rights. The National Organization for Women worked to help women get good jobs and equal pay. [Obj. 4.1]
19. Sample: They dismantled nuclear weapons. They worked on joint space missions. [Obj. 4.2]
20. civil rights
21. migrant worker
22. Peace Corps
23. arms race
24. suburb
25. Sample: the textbook, histories of the civil rights movement, a source that has Dr. King's speech.
26. Accept all reasonable questions, such as those asking for eyewitness accounts, personal reactions, and memorable moments in the march.
27. Sample: review tapes or notes; write what was learned in the interview.

Chapter 22 Test pg. 146

1. D [Obj. 1.1]
2. A [Obj. 1.1]
3. C [Obj. 1.2]
4. D [Obj. 1.2]
5. B [Obj. 2.1]
6. D [Obj. 2.1]
7. A [Obj. 2.2]
8. C [Obj. 2.2]
9. B [Obj. 3.1]
10. C [Obj. 3.1]
11. B [Obj. 3.2]
12. B [Obj. 3.2]
13. bilingual
14. petrodollar
15. infrastructure
16. tariff
17. Canadian Shield
18. A
19. E
20. He was describing the Canadian Shield. He didn't know that the Shield contains many valuable kinds of minerals. [Obj. 1.1]
21. Canada is mostly a nation of immigrants, with citizens who have come from all over the world. Citizens keep part of the culture of their heritage while sharing in a common Canadian culture. [Obj. 1.2]
22. Two mountain ranges run for hundreds of miles from north and south. The mountains have made it hard to ship goods. [Obj. 2.1]
23. It has made the economy grow. [Obj. 2.2]
24. Free trade gives people more choices about what they buy. The economies of participating countries can grow. [Obj. 3.1]
25. These organizations unite ordinary people from many countries in common efforts. They give people a chance to tackle problems directly. [Obj. 3.2]
26. The Eastern Hemisphere
27. The Western Hemisphere
28. In order to show the round world on a flat map, you must divide it. When map makers put the Eastern Hemisphere in the center, the United States is divided in half.
29. Most students will find Map B more familiar and suggest that we generally see the United States in the center of the map.

Unit 9 Open-ended Response pg. 151

Students should select an event from U.S. history in the twentieth century. The nature of the event and their own or their family's response to it should be correctly explained.